# INEQUALITIES IN HEALTH AND HEALTH PROMOTION: INSIGHTS FROM THE QUALITATIVE RESEARCH LITERATURE

*Anne Rogers, National Primary Care Research and Development Centre, University of Manchester*

*Jennie Popay, Gareth Williams and Melanie Latham, Public Health Research and Resource Centre, University of Salford*

© Health Education Authority, 1997
ISBN 0 7521 0890 5
Health Education Authority
Hamilton House
Mabledon Place
London WC1H 9TX

Printed in Great Britain by

# Contents

# Acknowledgements

Thanks are due to Professor Roy Carr-Hill (Senior Research Fellow), The University of York, who co-ordinated the components of the project.

The HEA is grateful for the support and contributions provided by the Advisory Group:

Professor Mildred Blaxter (University of East Anglia)
Dr Kathie Binysh (Department of Health)
Dr Jacky Chambers (Director of Public Health, Birmingham)
Bernie Evans (Account Manager, HEA)
Ian Gray (Health Policy Officer, London Borough of Hackney)
Dominic Harrison (West Lancashire Health Promotion Agency)
Dr Mike Hughes (Head of Research, Barnados)
Dominic McVey (Head of Research, HEA)
Jean Spray (Business Team Director, HEA)
Dr Margaret Thorogood (London School of Hygiene and Tropical Medicine)
Hilary Whent (Senior Researcher, HEA).

Thanks are also due to Isobel Bowler (who has since left the HEA) and Helen King who were involved in the early development of the work and to four anonymous peer reviewers.

# Foreword

The Health Education Authority (HEA) is a special health authority within the National Health Service. It advises government and undertakes research, consultation and policy development in support of national and local health promotion activity. This report is the first of three, which has emanated from a programme of HEA work looking at inequalities in health and the implications for health promotion. This began in 1995 and was the beginning of a programme of exploratory research which is now feeding into the HEA's new research strategy for tackling inequalities (Gillies and McVey, 1996).

There has been renewed interest in the topic of social inequalities in health, particularly as a result of the debate generated by the publication in 1980 of the Black Report (DHSS, 1980); this was followed up by *The Health Divide* (Whitehead, 1987) which was published in 1987 by the Health Education Council. In 1995, the Chief Medical Officer's Variations Sub-group published its report which recommended that the Department of Health and the NHS should give greater attention to variations in health (Department of Health, 1995). The new Minister of State for Public Health has indicated that the Government is committed to tackling the inequalities that lead to ill health (Department of Health, 1997).

The aim of the HEA's study was threefold. First it set out to provide an overview of variations in patterns of health behaviour among vulnerable groups; second, to develop a better understanding of the social and cultural determinants of variations in health behaviour and thirdly to support the commissioning of health promotion services and programmes aimed at reducing inequalities in health.

The project consisted of four components:

- a literature review of qualitative research on health behaviour and health promotion in the context of social variation in health.

- a consultation exercise with health professionals working at various levels, from grassroots to the level of strategic planning, to record their experience working with people who are disadvantaged in relation to health status.

- a review of the effectiveness of health promotion interventions aimed at reducing inequalities in health.

- analysis of several survey data-sets to explore patterns and determinants of health behaviour.

Much of the research which addresses inequalities in health is quantitative. This report focuses on the review of qualitative research carried out by Dr Anne Rogers and colleagues.

Qualitative research offers the opportunity to illuminate the subjective meaning of people's experiences and behaviour and to explore the links between knowledge, action and wider social and economic circumstances. In the context of inequalities in health, qualitative research helps to explain why some approaches in health promotion fail to reach the most vulnerable in society. This review reinforces views already held by many working in health promotion; that we need to take account of the material and social contexts in which people may or may not adopt healthier lifestyles; we need to consider the differing perspectives on health which professionals and lay people might hold; we need to consider harnessing lay people as a resource for health promotion and we need to carry out more research in order to deepen our understanding of the meanings and contexts in which people experience health.

The authors of this review have also begun urgently needed developmental work in identifying markers by which qualitative research may be judged. In the context of carrying out systematic reviews of research to inform health policy and service development, there has been much work which sets out criteria for assessing quantitative research, without parallel developmental work for qualitative research. The authors discuss the use of markers when selecting studies for their review. This work will support others who are carrying out reviews of qualitative research and it is hoped will encourage a debate about how research should be judged.

Hilary Whent
Senior Researcher
Health Education Authority

DHSS (1980). *Inequalities in Health: Report of a Research Working Group*. [Black Report].

Department of Health (1995). *Variations in Health: What can the Department of Health and the NHS do?* Report produced by the Variations Sub-Group of the Chief Medical Officer's Health of the Nation Working Group.

Department of Health (1997). New mission to tackle inequalities that lead to ill health. Tessa Jowell, press release, 97/095.

Gillies, P and McVey, D (1996). *Research for Health Promotion. A research strategy for the Health Education Authority for England 1996–99*. Health Education Authority.

Whitehead, M (1987). *The Health Divide*. Health Education Council.

# Introduction

This report is concerned to review the qualitative research literature on health behaviour and health promotion in the context of social variations in health. General information on the social patterning of mortality and morbidity is not included. This information has recently been succinctly summarised in a report from the Chief Medical Officer's Health of the Nation sub-group (Department of Health, 1995) and does not need to be revisited here. Aspects of lifestyle and health-related behaviour are frequently highlighted in attempts to explain these variations, particularly those variations associated with social class and geography. The evidence available suggests that social groups and geographical areas with the poorest health experience are also those with the highest rates of potentially health-damaging behaviour (for example smoking and drinking) and lowest rates of potentially health-enhancing behaviour (for example, exercise) (Blaxter et al., 1990). However, in recent years, the role of the social and material aspects of people's lives as an important factor in the understanding of the genesis and persistence of action relevant to health states has been recognised. This has been highlighted particularly in qualitative research and provides the background to this report.

The work reported here was commissioned by the Health Education Authority as part of a wider review of the implications of existing research for health promotion policy and practice. This report is divided into three parts. Part I consists of the substantive literature review. There are large areas of work to do with professional perspectives on health variations and the role of the media which we have not covered in any detail, and have only made reference to these areas of work in so far as they illuminate our central concern. Although most of the research reviewed makes use of qualitative methods, it is as much the approach to the understanding of daily life experience with health and illness that is important. As the extensive bibliography illustrates, a considerable literature has been covered. However, although the review draws widely on this in identifying important issues for health promotion, it does not make reference to, or discuss in detail, all of this work. Rather, selected studies have been used as examples of themes evident in the wider literature. In selecting these exemplars we have attempted to use a set of markers for quality standards in qualitative research. These are discussed in Part II of this report. These markers constitute a developing framework for assessing research standards and we have not had the time or resources to apply them comprehensively to all of the studies identified. Some of the studies included in our bibliography would not stand up to scrutiny as research which 'places at the forefront of enquiry lay understandings of the subjective meanings of health and health behaviour'. Part III consists of a technical report in which there is a discussion of the literature review methodology used.

# PART I: Understanding health-related action: Insights from qualitative research

# Key concepts in health promotion policy and practice

The concepts of 'lifestyle', 'risk' and 'preventive health behaviour' are terms central to the discourse of health promotion, and they form the primary focus of this review. The meaning of these commonly used terms varies across disciplines and professions. By way of introduction to the literature review, therefore, some discussion of the way these concepts are understood and used within health promotion policy and practice is necessary.

## Lifestyle

The word lifestyle is used frequently in everyday speech, in the mass media and in professional journals. Any strict definition of the term is bound to give rise to disagreement. However, Giddens (1991) refers to lifestyle as a 'cluster of habits and orientations' which provide a sense of ontological security around identity in a risk-laden society. Within the health arena there has been a growing appeal to the usefulness of 'lifestyle' as a conceptual tool to help inform policy and practice (WHO, 1986). The main advantages are seen to be the potential it offers for developing a holistic approach to understanding and responding to factors that both adversely affect and positively enhance health. In particular, it is argued, it allows for the incorporation of the ecological aspects of people's lives and for the consideration of the complex interrelationships between structurally and environmentally based 'chances', personal 'choices' and cultural contexts within which the relationship between chances and choices is lived out (Backett and Davison, 1995).

However, there has been criticism of the way in which health promotion in the UK and elsewhere has taken on board the lifestyle model. For example, it has been argued that much current policy and practice fails to address the importance of social context, subjective meaning and systematic influences on lifestyle 'choices' (Coreil, Levin and Jaco, 1985; Backett and Davison, 1995). Instead, a focus on individual responsibility has remained central and 'lifestyle' is used at its crudest to refer to a set of 'typical' individual or group behaviours. Thus the notion of 'lifestyle' has tended to stand as a convenient summary for those aspects of personal behaviour which make individuals more or less likely to develop diseases such as coronary heart disease or cancer – particularly, smoking, drinking, eating, exercise and unsafe sex.

Within professional health promotion the notion of 'risk' mediates the adoption and maintenance of certain lifestyles and/or behaviours in the pursuit of health and the prevention of disease. In the context of discussions of the variations in health literature, 'risk' and 'behaviour' have a position of growing importance over the last decade. In the Black Report on inequalities in health (DHSS, 1980), behavioural or cultural explanations were recognised to be important, but were very much secondary to materialist or structural explanations. However, recent work has tended to combine the two explanations providing a more sophisticated understanding of the link between social/structural factors and individual human agency in shaping health-related behaviours and lifestyles (Blaxter, 1990).

At the same time, a different trend can be identified within the medical/health literature, where a rapid increase in the use of the term 'risk', as applied to individual health behaviour in epidemiological studies, has been noted. It is argued that this 'epidemic' in research about risk may reflect a wider shift in belief systems in which the constructs of 'health' and 'risk' have moved from being linked to factors outside of human control to factors which can be controlled, often by changes in individual attitude and behaviour (Dean, 1994; Skolbekken, 1995). As Karen Lane has recently argued, 'risk has been assigned to individuals, rather than structural and social conditions' (Lane, 1995).

## Preventive health behaviour

Much relevant empirical research and health promotion activity has viewed health behaviour as the opposite of illness behaviour. This dichotomy is evident in an article by Kasl and Cobb (1966) who suggested that:

> Health behaviour is any activity undertaken by a person believing himself [sic] to be healthy, for the purpose of preventing disease or detecting it in an asymptomatic stage.

This minimalist definition fits some of the activities and procedures of health professionals, such as health check-ups and immunisation schedules (Pill and Stott, 1985a). However, this restricted definition has to an extent been superseded by attempts over the last two decades to develop a multi-dimensional approach to the notion of preventive health behaviour, incorporating practices and behaviours which involve individuals in day-to-day lifestyle choices (Langlie, 1977; Harris and Guten, 1979). In spite of this broadening of the concept, the idea of prevention remains oriented primarily to individual choice and change (Freeman, 1993). Within this orientation, health professionals play the role of ascetics, encouraging moderation and restraint in a life assumed to be tending towards excessive consumption of food, alcohol, tobacco and sex.

## *The structure of the review*

Qualitative research highlights the complexity, diversity and interconnectedness of the factors shaping health behaviour and lifestyle 'choices' . This is captured in a concluding comment by Pill and Stott, on the results of their work on health behaviours in South Wales in the early 1980s:

> Our results reveal that a cascade of socio-demographic factors, beliefs and attitudes are important and the mix of these antecedent factors will differ for the various preventive behaviours. It is now unlikely that a single variable, as yet un-researched, will be found which will reduce the level of unexplained variance substantially; instead we anticipate an increasingly complex situation, with any new variables making a small additional impact on the developing theoretical understanding for preventive behaviours. This leaves about 80% of the variance open to situational factors (Pill and Stott, 1985b, p. 981).

In order for health promotion policy and practice to rise to the challenge posed by social variations in health in contemporary society then greater attention needs to be given to the interface between social structure and human agency. This requires finding new ways of accommodating, and engaging with, the diversity and complexity that arises from incorporating the social context and subjective meaning of people's everyday lives. In reviewing the qualitative literature we have sought to highlight the extent and nature of this diversity and complexity. Discussions of the themes to emerge with the review are presented in the next section. They have been organised under four main headings:

1. a comparison of lay and professional perspectives

2. lay assessment of risk and health behaviour

3. coping and control

4. roles, practices and situations.

The last two sections of this part of the report then consider the implications for policy and practice, and summarise the key messages arising from the review as a whole.

# Themes emerging from the review

## 1. Comparing lay and professional perspectives

The relationship between 'lay' and 'professional' knowledge is a complex one within the literature. On the one hand, lay and professional perspectives on health, disease and risk have been shown to differ markedly in the context of both clinical care and public health. At the same time, there is evidence of convergence between lay and professional perspectives – in terms of dominant social values, the medical model and the importance of a holistic approach. Lay people may share dominant values to a greater extent than is often assumed by professionals, although these may be interpreted in different ways in terms of behaviour. The review has also highlighted the importance of pleasure as a factor shaping health behaviour amongst different lay groups. Two other aspects of the relationship between lay and professional knowledge emerge from the literature: the importance of recognising that professionals are lay people too and the influence exerted by the media in both publicising differences in views about health and health behaviour and in promulgating official views of appropriate interventions.

### (a) The grounded nature of lay perspectives

Qualitative research has consistently found that lay respondents make regular allusions to biographical, social and cultural factors in order to explain health status and behaviour (Blaxter and Paterson, 1982; Cornwell, 1984; Williams and Wood, 1986). In contrast, for professionals the principal referents in research and practice concerning healthy behaviours are derived from the secondary socialisation in training which emphasises formal bio-medical and epidemiological approaches to understanding health behaviour. Whilst lay views emphasise the interconnectedness of everyday life, health experience and behaviour, professional perspectives tend to fragment specific aspects of behaviour and neglect social context. Additionally, lay accounts highlight positive or 'natural' dimensions of behaviours/lifestyle whilst professional perspectives tend to problematise them.

Differences between lay and professional perspectives are evident along a number of dimensions. In a recently published study, for example, people's actions and attitudes about lifestyle were found to be closely associated with notions of life course (Backett and Davison, 1995). Lay perspectives developed in the context of the discernible cultural allocation of particular behaviours to age, demographic position and personal biography. In contrast to this 'grounded' lay perspective, a distinctive medicalised view can be discerned in much professional discourse in which aspects of lifestyle and life course are rendered problematic. The 'medical-isation' process identified by critics of medicine such as Zola (1972), can be seen as a decontextualisation of lay experience. In relation to infant and child health, for example, the socio-historical work of Wright (1987) has shown how baby and infant rearing became defined as a 'medico-technical' field, and similar analyses have been undertaken for childhood (Mayall *et al.*, 1993 and Pu, 1986).

Whilst the basis for professional and lay perspectives on many salient issues in health promotion may differ, it is important not to draw these distinctions too simplistically. As qualitative studies highlight, convergence and divergence co-exist across the professional/lay divide.

## (b) Shared values but different interpretations

Qualitative research suggests that for professionals to assume that the behaviour of particular groups in the population is informed by values different from those dominant in society may be inaccurate. However, there could be important differences, beyond any consensus over wider societal values, in the finer grain interpretation of issues. That is to say, societal values may be shared between professionals and lay groups but they may not be applied by lay people in a way which coincides with the expectations represented in an official health view.

For example, in a study examining practices deemed to be associated with sexually transmitted disease amongst prostitutes (Balshem *et al.*, 1992), while recognising STD as a risk associated with having sex with multiple partners, the respondents viewed themselves as adhering to dominant cultural values regarding cleanliness, morality and sexual behaviour. Images of cleanliness used by the respondents alluded to physical hygiene and notions of moral character which they deployed when identifying potential sexual partners. The finding that this group of sex workers appeal to the same moral discourse as those represented in wider American society points to the limitations of assuming that certain deviant groups are different culturally from 'the rest of us'.

A further example from the qualitative AIDS literature of the juxtaposition of consensus and divergence is a study by Lowy and Ross (1994) of perceptions of risk amongst homosexually active men. There was considerable overlap between lay and professional epidemiological knowledge, with, for example, large numbers of partners and a past history of unprotected anal intercourse being identified as major risk markers. However, at the same time the men based their notion of sexual risk on a configuration of activities in which there were few absolutes contrary to the differentiation of safe, safer and unsafe classifications used by health educators. The men also used risk markers such as age, appearance and diction which fall outside the traditional 'professional' signifiers of risk.

Similarly, in the study of accidents by Roberts, Bryce and Smith (1993) both parental and professional groups agreed that the maintenance of safety is a parental responsibility. Parents interviewed expressed commitment to the exercise of parental and collective responsibility in this regard and there was a recognition that mistakes were inevitably made. Additionally, a small proportion of families were considered to act irresponsibly. Where the lay and professional groups diverged was in their views on the part played by institutions and persons other than parents in relation to responsibility. Professionals viewed themselves as having a responsibility to educate parents. Parents on the other hand stressed that, in addition to themselves, the effective maintenance of child safety was a main responsibility of the local authority, housing agencies and officials associated with British Rail and building firms. Whilst acknowledging a generalised social responsibility for accidents, professionals rarely linked problems to specific agencies in the same way as the group of parents interviewed.

Other researchers have also suggested that medical encounters act to marginalise the context of problems and reinforce ideologies of stoicism and individualism. Waitzkin and Britt (1993), for example, examined everyday encounters between doctors and patients to assess how subjects such as smoking, substance abuse and sexual practices were broached. Through an analysis of conversations, they concluded that when the conversations turned to risk-taking behaviour, the patient was diverted by 'explicit pronouncements and implicit discouragements' from speaking of their social circumstances and how these might influence and constrain health behaviour. Waitzkin and colleagues (1994) came to the same conclusions in their study of consultations between doctors and older patients.

## (c) The medical model: an area of convergence

A number of qualitative researchers have drawn attention to the symbiotic relationship between medical and lay constructs of health, illness and health care. Early work on 'lay beliefs', for example, identified the impact of medical knowledge on lay beliefs about aetiology and the easy co-existence of this knowledge with that based on biography and experience (Helman, 1983; Williams and Wood, 1986). More recent work points to the persistence of this overlap. In a UK study of lay views on positive mental health, for example, some respondents expressed what De Swann (1990) has termed 'protoprofessionalised' views about psychological well-being (Rogers, Pilgrim and Latham, 1996). This involved a combination of medical and psychological terms and understanding, operating alongside a 'lay view'. It was not uncommon, for example, for respondents to use terms such as reactive or clinical depression or other diagnostic terms alongside more layified notions, for instance expressions such as 'a quagmire of worrying about yourself'. This type of 'protoprofessionalised' response was present to some extent in most accounts but was most notable in people whose occupational background entailed the use of psychological notions, such as buying, advertising or care work.

The cross-cultural nature of the overlap between medical and lay constructs of illness is indicated by a recent study of patients consulting primary care services in Finland. This showed a predominance of biomedical illness explanations amongst the patients studied (Punamaki and Kokko, 1995). Although a number of respondents referred to philosophical, metaphysical, psycho-social and lifestyle and risk behaviour, the most common explanation for their consultation related to infectious, toxic and noxious agents and constitutional defects in the body.

## (d) Moving towards holism

Though not a prominent theme in the literature, there is also some evidence that there may be a diminishing distance between some professional groups and lay populations with regard to the need for a more holistic approach to health problems. Not surprisingly perhaps, qualitative (and quantitative) research in the area of complementary therapies has suggested this for some considerable time (Sharma, 1993). There is now evidence to suggest that this perspective may extend beyond the marginal market-place of the complementary therapies. A recent example of this type of work is a Canadian study in which family physicians' perceptions about interventions for alcohol use were explored (Rush et al., 1995). Qualitative data collected from focus groups and semi-structured interviews indicated strong support for seeing alcohol use as a lifestyle issue which needed to be dealt with in 'the context of a holistic approach to patient care'. These patient-centred family physicians indicated that they did not feel it always appropriate to ask their patients about alcohol use. Frustration was also expressed over the 'lack of a systematic strategy or tangible materials to help them identify and manage patients'. This suggests that holistic ways of working may in some contexts make GPs more sensitive to the need to incorporate lay perspectives relating to health behaviour and risk.

## (e) The significance of pleasure in health behaviour

As we have indicated, lay perspectives on health and illness operate within wider symbolic universes of meaning. These universes incorporate values and judgements about what makes life worth living, and which factors create pleasure and which engender pain. The contextualisation or 'grounding' provided by lay perspectives allows for a perspective on behaviour which acknowledges its meaning. Behaviours which are seen from the 'outside' as negative or unhealthy may be seen from within as positive and pleasurable. Specific dimensions of health behaviour are frequently represented in health promotion in a moralistic and largely negative way. This can contrast sharply with lay narratives. Discussions of food and eating in everyday language across cultures, for instance, are often filled with expressions of epicurean enjoyment (Wood, 1995). For young women diet is strongly related to attractiveness and having boyfriends and girlfriends (Backett and Davison, 1995). In the context of traditional working class households, a 'good table' is one that is well stocked rather than one which displays the virtues of abstinence (Wight, 1993).

Studies of specific aspects of health behaviours often neglect the rich meanings attaching to everyday language in the area. In relation to food and eating, for example, while 'diet' carries the meaning of restraint, 'nutrition', 'eating', 'having a meal' and so on have a range of different meanings informing everyday behaviour in different situations and circumstances. Professional views of the risks attaching to particular dietary 'habits' bear little relationship to the ordinary ways of speaking about 'diet' in everyday life that have been highlighted in qualitative research. Within quantitative health research concepts such as 'dietary lapse' and 'calorie violation' may be related to 'situational determinants', but these are not usually derived from, or related back to, frameworks of subjective meanings or material circumstances.

In this context diet as a threat to health rather than a source of enjoyment is incongruous and the scope for direct appeals on health grounds is likely to have limited impact even in a society where consciousness about individual health is considered to have reached epidemic proportions. For example, research in Denmark involving in-depth interviews with young educated people about conforming to a recommended diet, found that whilst they did not object to its palatability they identified practical difficulties in applying it to everyday life outside the intervention (Holm, 1993).

Whilst this discussion has focused particularly on diet and food, the significance of pleasure as a feature of other aspects of behaviour relevant to health, notably smoking, sex and sexuality, the use of tobacco, alcohol and other drugs, and other forms of physical and mental leisure and recreation, substance use and exercise, is evident in the qualitative literature (Coggans-McKellar, 1994; Eiser *et al.*, 1989).

## (f) Heterogeneity in lay perspectives

In focusing on similarities and differences in the perceptions of professional/official and lay people, it is important not to neglect the diversity that exists within these two worlds and the overlap between them.

The number and complexity of views about health and the experience of illness, which may exist in one geographical locality and between lay groups have been highlighted by a number of studies. In relation to specific disease-related risk, for example, a recent study examining structure and meaning in models of breast and cervical cancer found considerable differences amongst groups of women and physicians in one area of California (Chavez et al., 1995). Immigrants from El Salvador and Mexico had a model of cancer risk that differed from those of both Anglo-American women and American physicians. Those from minority ethnic groups born in the US were described as 'bi-cultural' in their views with some overlap between immigrant and Anglo-American women but little with the physicians' views. While there was general agreement about the risks and prognosis of breast cancer between the groups, there was far less consensus for risk factors pertaining to cervical cancer. Mexican and Salvadorian women were much more likely to list physical trauma risk factors, such as miscarriages, having many children, childbirth, birth control devices and operations in the vaginal area, as risk factors.

This piece of research also shows that even when there is agreement on specific risk factors between different lay groups and professionals (for example, the risk posed by multiple sexual partners) there may be underlying differences in logic. For example, there was a consensus between groups that multiple sexual partners constituted a risk factor in relation to cervical cancer. However, for the Latino immigrant group, multiple sexual partners resonated with moral considerations, whilst for medical practitioners it raised the probability of infection from sexually transmitted diseases.

Differences between lay groups have also been shown in relation to childhood accidents (in this case strongly linked to social class and material circumstances). In-depth interviews were held with parents from two geographical areas: one with a high accident rate and the other with a low rate. This study points to the importance of differential social class 'rules', 'routines' and 'practices' in keeping children safe (Sparks, Craven and Worth, 1994). Parents across social class divisions saw teaching their children as a taken for granted part of parenting. However, there were different social class perceptions of parental capacity to keep children safe and about who had responsibility for that safety. Middle-class parents, most of whom lived in the low accident rate area, were more likely than working-class parents to refer to social and personal factors as the major reasons for low accident rates in the area. They also gave greater salience to the nature of parenting and parental surveillance. In contrast the working-class parents from the high accident area focused on threats from the environment and not the nature and quality of parenting as the main factors explaining the high accident rate of the area. These differences suggest a realistic appraisal of safety practices and routines on the part of parents (rather than differences in 'locus of control') and point to the importance of the broader social, structural, material and cultural resources in shaping differences in social class-based behaviours and practices.

## (g) The professional as a lay person

Throughout this review, a distinction has been drawn between professional and lay views. However, just as it can be argued that lay people can develop a role as 'experts' in problems with which they become concerned, so professionals are not only professionals – they too, have a lay perspective grounded in their own experience. However, there is a sense in which these lay aspects of their understanding become bracketed out as they practice their professional roles. They may develop what Merton (1957) has referred to as a 'trained incapacity' to see things in the way they once saw them. However, the co-existence of a lay/professional perspective does provide the possibility for developing ways of fostering some convergence between lay and professional views in health promotion.

There are a considerable number of doctors who have written from personal experience as poets or novelists or, less grandly, have simply talked or written about their experiences of health and illness. Professionals, too, take or find themselves exposed to risks, get ill, and die, and these experiences challenge more than just their professional knowledge. The *British Medical Journal* and other professional publications sometimes include comment and analysis on professionals' own experiences, testifying to the symbiosis between their lay and professional views. Nurses and doctors may feel that it is both their professional knowledge and the lay intellectual resources that reach limits when they themselves are confronted with the prospect of chronic illness or death.

The relative weight given to the lay and professional views by an individual is dependent on the context as well as the content of such views/constructs. For example, in a recent study of non-compliance with immunisation, a number of health professionals who were strong advocates of the mass childhood immunisation programme, provided similar accounts to those given by dissenting non-professional mothers, for not having their own children fully vaccinated (Rogers and Pilgrim, 1994). However, professionals often find it difficult to adopt the lay perspective where the context is one in which their professional judgement is expected and tested.

## (h) The media as mediator

Differences (and similarities) between professional and lay views are to an extent influenced by the mass media. The media play an important part in both the mediation and construction of views about health behaviour. Recent qualitative work in Australia has examined the dissemination and reception of professional and official views of health behaviour. Lupton (1995) analysed the coverage of medical and health stories in a 'quality' Australian newspaper over a one-year period. Examining a combination of the topics, visual imagery and content of news stories, she found that issues to do with health service delivery far outweighed those related to health prevention/promotion or behaviour. For both sets of topics she found that coverage was:

> predominantly conservative, giving greater voice to elite groups than less powerful groups such as advocacy, activist and community groups, and to men rather than women. It tended to individualise illness rather than place it in its broader social, economic and political contexts (p. 501).

Thus, in relation to tobacco and smoking, smokers were portrayed as 'sickly deviants – literally a "dying breed"' which is consistent with the official view on smoking but as is evident elsewhere in this review, not necessarily with lay views.

Lay views about risk and lifestyle in relation to diet may also be mediated by the mass media. Information on cholesterol and salt intake in relation to health as represented in the media has been examined in relation to lay views. For example, in one study using content analysis of press coverage of the cholesterol 'controversy' and focus group discussions it was found that while people may respond with concern to messages about the need to change diet, there is also a high degree of cynicism both about the content of the media messages and the content of the health promotional advice on which the media draw (Lupton and Chapman, 1995). In this work it is clear that while 'control' over eating is recognised to be important, it is also understood that eating is a form of pleasure which brings 'release' from the constraints of everyday life. Moreover, in response to the often conflicting messages about diet, people may fall back upon the folk wisdom of 'everything in moderation' as a means of reconciling personal conflicts over diet.

## 2. Lay assessment of risk and health behaviour

### (a) The contribution of qualitative research

Qualitative research into the meanings lay people attach to their experiences and actions add details to the existing picture we have of how people assess risks to health and why they behave as they do in response to these. First, it highlights the importance of social context in risk assessment; second, it points to the complex relationship between knowledge about health hazards and action at a group and/or individual level to prevent/reduce them; third, it suggests that some groups of lay people are increasingly sceptical about the legitimacy of formal scientific knowledge about the determinants of health and illness; and fourth, it highlights the way in which attitudes to risk and the control of risk are components of complex, interpersonal, social and material processes to which individuals are constrained to respond.

## (b) The context of lay risk assessment

Lay assessment of risk and appraisal of health is a feature of health behaviour high-lighted by a number of studies. Social commentators such as Mary Douglas (1992) and Anthony Giddens (1991) point out that in a society dominated by expert risk assessors (of whom medical practitioners are an example) ordinary people are frequently thought to lack the capacity to reason probabilistically. However, as Douglas points out, lay people have always made calculations about risks and chances based on many factors in the environment including (though not exclusively) scientific information. Qualitative studies have made a contribution to examining how individuals develop their own, and at times, dissenting view of disease aetiology, assessments of risk and formulation of health problems.

Backett and Davison (1995), for example, explored the way in which people make judgements about their health by comparing two UK studies on common-sense assessments of everyday health-related behaviour. Notions of lifecourse were deployed by respondents to express and encapsulate health-relevant behaviours and lifestyles. Lay evaluations were noted to occur in the context of 'the perceived cultural appropriateness of the behaviour to age, demographic position and personal biography'. Three stages of the life course were identified with specific health-relevant behaviours and lifestyles. These covered a twenty-five-year span, young and single, married with no children and married with children. The first of these life stages was associated with one's body being at its physical peak and with the idea that the 'youthful body' was able to achieve an equilibrium, what-ever unhealthy food was eaten or activities were undertaken. Positive action about lifestyle was viewed as most appropriately taken at another later life stage when because of one's age the body was not as resilient as it is in youth. Many respondents felt that it was boring to be preoccupied with healthy lifestyles and chronic illness. A different orientation to illness assessment and avoidance tended to emerge with new social expectations, experiences and responsibilities. In the two later life stages illness assessments were overlain with normative moral consideration, such as having a partner, mortgage and children.

In another study Richards (1993) points out that lay beliefs about the inheritance of risk are at variance with 'Mendelian' theories of geneticists (or 'dominant' professional views). The extent to which people feel prone to genetic disease provides an explanation for the uptake of genetic services. This resonates with the work of Davison *et al.* (1991) on coronary candidacy – i.e. that self-assessment of individual risk or 'proneness' is crucial to understanding the reasons for risk- (or non-risk-) avoiding behaviours.

## (c) The relationship between knowledge and action

Many studies, using both quantitative and qualitative approaches, have highlighted the complex nature of the relationship between knowledge of risk and action to prevent or reduce risk. There are certainly studies which show that some vulnerable groups lack basic information about the hazards of behaviours/practices in which they are involved. But it is also clear that adequate knowledge about the nature of risks associated with particular behaviours is not a sufficient or necessary determinant of behaviour change. Hilary Graham's work on smoking patterns amongst women, for example, is an illustration of this point. Despite having full knowledge of the risks they were exposing themselves to, women living in poverty were highly likely to continue to smoke (Graham, 1987).

Similarly, in the study discussed earlier on non-compliance with childhood immunisation, parents interviewed were found to be knowledgeable about the aetiology, nature and prognosis of infectious childhood diseases such as tetanus, diphtheria, measles, rubella, and whooping cough. However, they failed to make the same connections as health promoters in relation to preventing the diseases. Whilst the behaviour sought by health professionals was centred on immunisation uptake, dissenting parents were not satisfied that vaccination was the best way to protect their children's health, preferring to opt for other strategies of health maintenance, such as homoeopathic remedies, prolonged breast feeding and exposure to children with measles (Rogers and Pilgrim, 1995). The research on lay views about safe sex discussed above also demonstrates considerable overlap between lay and professional constructs about risky behaviour (Lowy and Ross, 1994; Balshem et al., 1992). Similarly, in a recent study of lay perspectives on health hazards/risks in an inner city area in the north-west of England, the nature and extent of risks to health associated with aspects of individual behaviour and the material environment were clearly understood and articulated by respondents. However, there was no evidence of either collective or individual action to change things (Williams, Popay and Bissell, 1995).

There is also evidence in the literature of a growing scepticism amongst lay publics concerning the status of professional/scientific knowledge as the only or most important arbiter on the nature and significance of risk. In the study of views of health risks in the inner city, for example, respondents voiced considerable dissatisfaction with the performance of local professionals as assessors of risk (Williams, Popay and Bissell, 1995). Similarly, a number of studies have shown how local communities are questioning the status of scientific evidence on the link between ill health and exposure to environmental hazards (Brown, 1995; Brown and Masterson-Allen, 1994; Wing, 1994).

## (d) Fatalism and realism: attitudes as social processes

As with aspects of lifestyle such as food and eating, risk has been understood differently across the lay/official health divide. Sklobekken (1995) points out that it is only relatively recently that risk has come to be seen as produced by human agency – as side effects of developments that are viewed as beneficial (hence the notion of 'illnesses of affluence'). This 'relocation' of the site of risk within individuals has meant that previously widely held fatalistic notions about health and illness have been replaced, in some quarters at least, by an ideology which emphasises the possibilities of control over life and death and an attendant struggle to identify and eliminate risk. This manifestation of 'possessive individualism' has led to a situation in which those who do not see risks as controllable can be blamed for their fatalistic attitudes.

Within health psychology, for example, there is a substantial body of work using concepts such as 'locus of control' and 'self-efficacy'. In most psychological work these concepts are applied to the attitudes and behaviours of individuals, with little attention paid to social context except as extraneous variance. A further weakness of psychological models of health behaviour is a tendency to attribute too much importance to the individual's perceptions of risk at the expense of other variables (Bloor, 1995).

In contrast, there is now a growing body of qualitative work which has explored different aspects of people's perceptions of 'fate' and 'control', helping us to understand the social processes within which attitudes are shaped and sustained, including individualistic attitudes to explaining the links between health and daily life. A number of researchers have pointed to the tendency for people living in the most disadvantageous circumstances to be more likely than the better off to accept individualistic causal models of health and behaviour (Calnan, 1983; Blaxter, 1985).

Research carried out by Davison, Davey Smith and Frankel (1991) identified fatalistic (and realistic) attitudes towards the risks posed by CHD in a lay population in South Wales. These findings are similar to the attitudes uncovered in other lay populations, in South Wales nearly two decades earlier and in Scotland some 30 years ago. These studies also indicated that fatalism about health was a prevalent theme – though not the only one – in working-class women's lives (Blaxter and Paterson, 1982; Pill and Stott, 1982; Pill and Stott, 1985). In all of these studies, notions of 'fatalism' are strongly tied to 'realism' in the lives of people living in poor material circumstances – that is fatalistic attitudes could be argued to be realistic assessments of the opportunities for control in people's lives.

In qualitative studies of both private and commercial sexual relationships, and parental perceptions of the safety of their children, there have been attempts to see perceptions of risk as part of complex interpersonal, social and material processes. The importance of focusing on risk assessment within the context of power in inter-personal relationships, for example, is indicated by a study by

Bloor (1995). He illustrates the inadequacy of traditional health behaviour models which place the individual centre stage with reference to sexual practices amongst commercial sex workers. Risk behaviour in relation to HIV involves, minimally, a prostitute and a client, and often a 'pimp' as well. 'With one exception all those engaging in commercial and anal sex did so because they were constrained to do so by clients' (Bloor, 1995).

Studies of private heterosexual encounters also report qualitative findings which suggest that unsafe sexual practices arise out of power relationships between men and women (Holland *et al.*, 1992). By adopting an emergent data-driven approach, qualitative research has therefore been instrumental in demonstrating the limitations of existing models of health behaviour and the potential utility of adopting a model which focuses on dyadic relationships, in particular, and social relationships more generally. Another example in this regard is the work on condom use. In-depth interviews were carried out with heterosexual men and women to understand the impact of dyadic behaviour on decisions to use condoms, partner support and receptivity to co-operate in safer sexual practices. Key findings were that the dialogues about condoms occur at both intrapersonal and interpersonal levels (Browne and Minichiello, 1994).

Realistic appraisal of the extent to which people are able to exercise personal control over threats to health is also illuminated in the study on parental perceptions of safety beliefs about accidents previously discussed. In a study of child accidents all parents interviewed developed rules and strategies to keep their children safe and to minimise the risk of accidents and injury. However, working-class parents living in areas which were objectively more hazardous – for example, in close proximity to busy main roads – were more likely to view environmental factors as more important in preventing childhood accidents than their own attempts at parental safety education (Sparks, Craven and Worth, 1994).

In their work on child accident prevention, Roberts and her colleagues (1993) found that parents saw accidents as one element of insecurity and hazard associated with living in damp, cold houses in areas with busy roads. Moreover traditionally accidents were not viewed as accidents at all in so far as the risks involved could be anticipated and were not therefore accidental. Instead, features of the environment, such as rotten balconies, were known hazards which would lead to injury. These hazards were, according to parental accounts, disregarded by official builders and planners. In the same study a frequently reported view amongst professionals was that people hold fatalistic views of child accidents which are not amenable to preventive activities. However, in some instances risks to children raised by parents, such as the dangerousness of roads, were down-played by health professionals.

Many other studies highlight a similarly significant role for others in relation to 'individual' risk assessment. In the context of dietary choices, for example, research has shown how women's decisions about the purchase and provision of food, as the key actors with regard to their own diet and that of other members of the household, are largely shaped by access to financial resources and the preferences of children and partners. Research into women's use of emergency medical care and primary care for young children, has also illuminated a decision-making process influenced by material resources, social relationships and past experience of a child's illness (Pearson *et al.*, 1993). Finally, research into smoking patterns amongst young people has identified an important though complex role for peer relationships.

What such studies lead us to conclude is that attitudes to personal behaviour and health must be seen as part of a social context; that the perspectives on which these attitudes are based are not linked in a simplistic way to the actions people take; and that context, behaviour, and attitude are part of interpersonal, social and material processes which individuals have to negotiate in their everyday lives.

## 3. Coping and control

### (a) Personal experience as a key mediating factor between agency and structure

As much of the research referenced so far indicates, personal experience constitutes a relevant focus for furthering our understanding of the relationship between social circumstances and individual behaviour. A number of studies have sought to take account of the interaction between agency and structure and between the material, the social and personal aspects of everyday life. Hilary Graham's work exploring smoking patterns and behaviours amongst women living in poor material circumstances in England is an example here. Using a combination of qualitative and quantitative methods her work has demonstrated how women living in difficult circumstances may consciously use cigarettes to cope with the stress and strains of daily life. Graham's work (1987), which involves a qualitative dimension, spotlighted the importance of the expression of personal experience in gaining insights into what, from an official perspective, would be categorised as health-damaging behaviour.

Applying this theme within our search revealed that personal experience as a mediating factor was a salient theme in a number of other studies. In a study of smoking amongst adolescent women, for example, the lack of social opportunities in the experiences of leisure led them to seek identification in alternatives (Wearing, Wearing and Kelly, 1994). In this context smoking was found to be both a type of resistance and a form of leisure activity. In another study the content of commonsense knowledge and its relationship to scientifically-based safer-sex guidelines amongst 25 Canadian college students was examined. For the young adults interviewed an overriding rule of HIV protection which pre-dominated was obtaining protection through the selection of uninfected partners (Matickatyndale, 1992). However, the *implementation* of this key rule varied according to gender and sexual experience. In relation to the former, a double standard was noted between men and women in relation to sexual activity which has implications for men's and women's ability to protect themselves and the personal construction of safer-sex strategies.

## (b) Swapping risks: lay cost/benefit analysis

The studies discussed in the above section, and research by others (Lewis and Ross, 1995; Mullen, 1992) indicates that at times assessments of risk may result in the adoption of one type of threat to health rather than another. For example, the use of party drugs rather than unsafe sex as in Mullen's study. This suggests that people may engage in a process akin to cost/benefit analysis. The problem facing health promoters in a case like this may be the unpalatability of accepting the sub-stitution of a less risky behaviour for one with a greater objective threat to health. In this case it would be the illegality of illicit drug taking. The same sort of dilem-ma underlay discussions about the introduction of needle exchange schemes in the mid-1980s.

Lay assessments about risks to physical and mental health may also lead to similar 'least cost' decisions. In-depth analysis of smoking and drinking behaviour in the Mullen study, for example, suggests these substances were used to relieve stress even though they were known to be physically health damaging. This phenomenon was also noted in the study on mental health by Rogers, Pilgrim and Latham (1996) referred to earlier . Similarly Umberson and Williams (1993) in their qualitative study of divorced parents found that respondents attempted to protect their mental health by taking risks with their physical health, for example by consuming alcohol or drugs, or by choosing outlets such as resorting to violence in social settings such as pubs or by attacking the source of their frustration – their ex-wives or ex-wives partners.

## (c) Coping strategies and personal control

Within the qualitative literature there are examples of the myriad innovative ways in which people struggle to compensate for, cope with and, where possible, control threats to their physical and mental health. A prominent strategy identified in several studies is 'disengagement'. This is illustrated in Mullen's study of the health behaviour of Glaswegian men in the context of paid employment. As

Mullen (1987) notes: 'interviewees highlighted forms of disengagement where they would consciously distance themselves from involvement in the work process'. This took the form of either physical or mental disengagement. As with the other studies on smoking reported in this review tobacco was also found to be an important means of coping with the pressures of work. Whilst this constituted a major coping strategy at work, outside of work alcohol served this function. Individuals also coped with negative health effects of work by adapting themselves to minimise risk or by attempting to control their environment by, for example, reorganising work tasks. The type of compensation and control exercised was related to the type of health effects produced by their occupation. For example, where a job's physical demands were low, diet and exercise were the focus of concern, whilst this was not the case where moderate physical activity was part of the job.

Another example which serves to illustrate the process of individual coping is provided by a study exploring the way in which young and middle-aged women experienced incontinence. Interviews revealed that the women felt that the problem was their own fault and experienced the fear associated with stigmatised and despised groups. Linked to this perception of self-responsibility was a means of coping which the psychodynamically orientated researchers labelled 'defensive denial' whereby individuals 'subordinated' the problem in favour of other priorities (Ashworth and Hagan, 1993). It is worth noting here that the prominence given to the researchers' interpretation of these women's subjective accounts may indicate that insights from women's own interpretations of their behaviour could have been missed.

A strategy of disengagement or problem avoidance has been noted in other qualitative studies. For example Umberson and Williams (1993) found that divorced men dealt with the perceived lack of control over their lives by avoiding contact with their ex-wives through avoiding contact with their children. Similarly, a study which drew on the personal accounts of female and male adolescents about body image and self-identity suggests that many young people experience 'disembodiment' in physical education lessons which in turn acted as a strategy for the protection of self-identity. This was particularly so for those who held perceptions of their own bodies which differed from the dominant stereotypes of the masculine or feminine body. In trying to make their way through the physical tasks set in the PE lessons a number of the respondents experienced alienation as they risked revealing their physical incompetence (Kirk and Tinning, 1994).

Another example of coping marked out by a number of studies is the use of normalisation strategies or, to coin a phrase from Goffman (1963) 'passing'. In this regard pain or threats to health are minimised by continuing in role and carrying out responsibilities. For example, a study of Puerto Rican men suffering from chronic pain found that the continuation of employment and normal routine activities was mediated by their strong sense of identity as bread winners (Bates and Rankin-Hill, 1994).

## (d) Social networks and support

In recent years one of the fastest growing fields of health research is that focusing on the significance of social support and social networks as health protecting and/or enhancing. Much of this research has been quantitative and is reviewed elsewhere (Oakley, 1993). A key theme to emerge from this literature and the small though significant number of qualitative studies, is that social networks may provide the sustenance for individual coping and control and may be particularly important in the context of poor material circumstances. Thus in future research on the factors associated with positive health behaviour changes, it may be more valuable for access to and quality of social networks/support to form the focus of analysis rather than individual traits, such as 'locus of control'. Put another way social networks and support might more fruitfully be viewed as the independent variable, with the actual style of coping and modes of individual control seen as the outcome.

Research to date has, for understandable reasons, focused on styles of coping with behavioural change as the outcome. One recent example of research which has placed social networks at the heart of understanding individual coping and control is provided by an ethnography of HIV prevention (Power et al., 1995). This study illuminates the way in which individual coping is sustained and maintained through co-operation and supportive mechanisms amongst injecting drug users not in contact with services. Another study, which illustrates the futility of predominantly viewing risk-taking as an individual matter or trait, investigated risk-taking behaviour and AIDS knowledge amongst pregnant and parenting adolescents in California. This research found that in addition to a number of factors affecting condom use – gender inequality, embarrassment, personal preference and values – risk-taking behaviour was influenced by 'a lack of security and safety in daily living, and peer pressure' (Koniak-Griffin et al., 1994).

## 4. The influence of roles, practices and situations

### (a) The general issues

In addition to highlighting the importance of personal experience as mediating between agency and structure, qualitative research has also pointed to the salience of particular roles, practices and situations. This is apparent at many different levels, for example, studies which have looked at the social context of diet have examined the role of women in families and the way in which roles promote or constrain 'personal nutrition care' (Devine and Olsen, 1992). Data from in-depth interviews with women 'homemakers' and women in employment outside the home indicate that social roles influence women's attitudes about personal nutrition care both 'positively' and 'negatively'. This influence is modified by women's changing interpretation of their roles at different life stages.

The intense focus on AIDS within the qualitative literature has had the advantage of enabling a detailed examination of discrete groups to take place in which the fine grain complexities of lay health knowledge have been made visible. This is exemplified by studies of the different sexual practices adopted by sex workers which show the importance of particularistic roles, practices and situations, in addition to locality, gender, region and class. For example, in comparing two ethnographic studies of prostitution carried out simultaneously in Glasgow in which female street-working prostitutes were compared with a group of male rent boys (McKeganey, Barnard and Bloor, 1990), two major differences were identified. First, injecting drug use was less frequent amongst male street workers than female counterparts. Second, rent boys were far less directive in relation to clients, and in particular much less likely to insist on safer sexual practices than the female prostitutes. This lack of directiveness was associated with the practice of retrospective payment for commercial sex in males compared to the traditional demand of prospective payment from female workers.

Assessment of threats to health can lead to changes in collective and individual practices which at times may feed into wider routinised practices – on the face of things these may have little direct relevance to health. This is illustrated by a study of the gay dance party phenomenon in Sydney ( Lewis and Ross, 1995) which noted the growing use of 'appropriately sited' dance venues with the attendant use of 'party drugs' and laser-lighting. The threat of HIV infection amongst gay men was identified as one factor amongst a number which had provided the context for a more ritualised set of social interactions. These fulfilled the social and psychological needs of gay men which have previously been met in a more uncontained and expressive gay lifestyle where private parties and inner-city gay bars had been primary meeting areas.

Another example of the importance of situation is provided by a study which examined the strains connected with care-giving which has traditionally been associated with a threat to psychological health. The findings suggested that the strains of care-giving were not confined to direct care-giving activities but were also related to 'established patterns of daily life' (Periard and Ames, 1993). Hilary Graham's most recent work on smoking amongst pregnant women also points to the importance of looking in more detail at the circumstances of different groups of poor women. Graham found that the poorer the woman, the more children she has, the poorer her health and that of her children, the more likely she is to (continue to) smoke. This work was largely quantitative, and qualitative research might usefully help to understand the processes lying behind this general pattern (Graham, 1993).

## (b) Gender

The significance of understanding the finer grain of gender and gender roles in relation to health behaviour is illustrated by a number of qualitative studies. Gendered construction of specific aspects of health provide insights into the importance of aspects of people's lives, such as sexuality, which are not decon-textualised or objectified into an all-encompassing global variable typical of quantitative research. For example, in one study, findings from 18 focus group discussions held with young male and female factory workers are discussed, with principal reference to gender and respondents construction of sexuality, in a context of growing intensity of threats to sexual health (Peterson and Johnstone, 1995). Health-related literature which concentrates on parental behaviour may not only mask the fact that most parental care is provided by mothers (Popay, Bartley and Owen, 1993) but that these groups hold varying values and beliefs which might result in different ways of acting. An example of 'hidden' gender differences is provided by a study which used focus groups to elicit inner city parental views about mental health prevention and alcohol and substance abuse amongst children. Mothers and fathers expressed widely varying views which led the authors to suggest the need to target preventative interventions separately at fathers and mothers (Lengua et al., 1992).

The importance of gendered roles in health behaviour is further illustrated by Anderson (1987) who examined Canadian and Greek women immigrants' health constructs in relation to their roles. She found that health-care ideologies and women's response to these were grounded in the ideology of women's role. There was a disjuncture between how women actually feel and how they were supposed to feel. Many women therefore found it difficult to figure out why they felt the way they did in relation to mental health. The focus of this work was help-seeking from professionals, but the findings may well be equally applicable to understanding how lay people receive and act upon health messages.

## (c) Class

Social class has been a major feature of the epidemiological and disciplinary work on variations in health, illness and death, although less significance has been given to lay definitions and views about this. Qualitative research highlights a number of key facets about class and its connectedness to health and health behaviour.

One area of importance in this regard is the world view which underlies the views and behaviours of people in different classes about health. An early path-breaking study was conducted by Herzlich (1969) in France. On the basis of analysing data from qualitative interviews carried out with members of the middle and 'intellectual' classes in Paris and Normandy she suggested that the social representation of health and illness was a combination of the lived experience of members of a social class and the values and information of society as a whole. This dual relationship (to society and to an individual's health and illness) is psychologically mediated. In making the formulation that illness is caused by the lifestyle imposed by society, the individual defends him or herself against both illness and society. (Whether this theory is transferable to a British context is a moot point given the differing political consciousness of the two nations.)

Using open-ended questions at the end of a large survey on the meaning of health conducted in the north-eastern part of France (Lorraine) d'Houtard and Field (1984) aimed to elicit people's 'image of health'. Forty-six themes were identified from the open-ended questions and then analysed quantitatively. In this regard this study is a synthesis of methodological traditions, but is included here because primacy is given to the subjective meanings expressed by respondents in the first instance. Linking the multiplicity of themes to social and economic class, major differences were found. The higher social class groups conceptualised health in personalised, positive and expressive terms, whilst the manual classes viewed them more in negative, socialised and instrumental terms. For the author these polar views were linked to individual position within the social order. The middle-class respondents reflected the realisation of an assured notion of self and sense of mastery over others and their own lives, whilst the working-class configuration of health and health behaviour reflected the 'integration of self into society and into the tasks which society demands of individuals' (p. 47).

## (d) Ethnicity

In the Anderson study (1987), which focused on immigrant women's constructs of health, ethnicity was found to overlay gender role issues and expectations in so far as the women had to contend with stereotypes and the way their health behaviour was perceived by health professionals. Ethnicity is also a key variable in the field of diet and health behaviour. This work has been particularly important in looking at the experience of people from minority ethnic groups with particular 'diet-related' chronic diseases such as diabetes. However, as this work suggests, detailed analysis of the interaction of a number of factors is necessary to understand behaviour and the lay management of ill health. Here, too, focus groups have been used to explore barriers to effective health promotion. In one study (Quatromoni et al., 1994), 'Caribbean Latinos' took part in focus groups in which participants with diabetes mellitus described the multiple barriers in daily life to diet and exercise interventions and, again, expressed scepticism with regard to the value of preventive health behaviours.

In their study looking at women from different ethnic backgrounds, Anderson *et al.*, (1995) found that management of diet and other factors in relation to diabetes was not reducible to ethnicity. Diabetes management is a multi-faceted phenomenon which has to be understood in relation to the mediating circumstances of a people's lives. 'Simple' health promotion messages therefore need to be understood in relation to this context.

A similar perspective emerges from in-depth qualitative analysis of the accounts of Asian women with regard to diet in pregnancy (Woollett *et al.*, 1995). While traditional cultural beliefs and practices were important, they also responded to Western maternity advice. Additionally an ethnographic study observing the interactions of midwives with pregnant and birthing Asian women suggested a clash between Western and Asian values, in particular over the construction of motherhood (Bowler, 1993). This, and other work suggests that it is important in promoting the health of Asian women in pregnancy to get away from stereotyped attitudes to religion and culture and explore the personal circumstances of individual women (Donovan, 1984, 1986; Bowes and Domokos, 1993).

## (e) Locality as cultural context and identity

The importance of locality has long been a prominent theme in health research. It is usual for quantitative studies to explore differences between geographical regions, electoral wards and enumeration districts. The level of analysis is usually determined by the data collection permitted by large and complex data-sets such as the Census. Qualitative studies, however, highlight different notions of locality which are important in understanding the adoption and maintenance of health-related behaviours. For example, as we have discussed elsewhere in this review, social networks are important mediators for coping strategies and risk reduction activities of individuals. From ethnographic observations Power *et al.* (1995) note major differences in the cultural context of localities which impinge on drug-users' social networks and which might, along conventional measures of rurality and socio-economic profile, appear similar:

> Due to the need for greater anonymity in the cases of the smaller populated sites of Midtown and Hertfordshire, no open-street scene existed, where drug users would congregate to sell, buy and consume drugs. This was in stark contrast to the London case, where a number of street scenes (many of which were well established) were fully functioning, trading in a range of drugs, such as heroin, cocaine and pharmaceutical preparations (Power *et al.*, 1995 p. 569).

# The implication of qualitative research for health promotion policy and practice

## The 'prevention paradox' and 'prevention contradiction' as disincentives to change individual behaviour

Official agencies responsible for health promotion and prevention generally assess risk at a *population* level. This contrasts with assessment about risk by *individuals*. At times a contradiction can exist between these two approaches to risk assessment and strategies aimed at reducing diseases at a population level may clash with the way in which individuals assess the risk of disease. Two qualitative studies are illustrative here (Davison, Davey Smith and Frankel, 1991; Rogers and Pilgrim, 1995). Davison and his colleagues illuminated how lay people come to assess the likelihood of becoming victims of heart disease with reference to personal experience and observations about other people they consider to be at risk. In particular, the notion of 'coronary candidacy' promoted by official health prevention campaigns is viewed as a fallible construct. Coronary heart disease and deaths were known to occur in persons who did not fit the official health risk profile. Similarly, it was noted that people with the official health risk profile did not always go on to develop heart disease. Within this context Davison and colleagues point out that as health promotion strategies become more and more successful, as judged by population target levels being met, then a 'prevention paradox' is encountered. The greater the success at the population level, the less health relevance there is at the individual level.

At times, this weighing up of benefits and disadvantages may lead people to see preventative messages as increasingly irrelevant to their particular situation. It may also create what might be termed a 'prevention *contradiction*'. This form of lay appraisal is evident in the study by Rogers and Pilgrim (1995) of the personal accounts of mainly middle-class women who dissented from including their children in the mass childhood immunisation programme. For these respondents, as childhood diseases, such as whooping cough and diphtheria, become less prevalent and new ways of protecting children against the contraction and adverse effects of disease are adopted, for example through healthy eating, and prolonged breast feeding, so the risk ratio gradually tilts in the direction of vaccines being seen as dangerous to individual recipients. The chance of iatrogenic vaccine damage is seen as being greater than the threat to their children of infectious disease. Dissenting parents then quite rationally opt to protect their children optimally from risk via non-compliance.

Such lay assessments on the part of relatively powerful groups of people (in this case mainly middle-class professional mothers) have potentially profound implications in an area where health inequalities exist. Assessment of risk by a group where alternative means of protection are feasible is a matter of choice. However, attempts by one group to reduce the risk that vaccination has for their children, may have the effect of increasing vulnerability of other groups where children are not well protected and which, for a variety of reasons, do not have access to alternative methods of protection.

## Health promotion and education – understanding failure and success

Qualitative studies can also help us to understand why health education initiatives may fail to change health-denying behaviour where the risks are agreed upon by both lay people and health professionals. Stone (1989) suggests the presence of an inverse prevention law whereby preventative activities receive official endorsement in reverse relation to their likely effectiveness. At times, these official risk reduction strategies require changes in the behaviour of potential victims of health hazards when more effective change could be brought about by a focus on those that produce risk. Roberts *et al.* (1993) summarises the problem with existing health education and its preoccupation with behavioural change succinctly when discussing child accidents:

> Traditional health education works on the premise that with the right information, skills and reinforcement, behaviour and health decisions may be changed . . . the White Paper *The Health of the Nation* draws on this approach, suggesting education as an important means of reducing accidents . . . The educational approach to accident prevention involves a deficit model of parents . . .

Roberts *et al.* showed in their research that the physical environment put children at risk and that parents were aware of these risks and took steps to keep their children safe. Smoking is an area where rates of change in behaviour are a constant challenge to health promoters, particularly amongst young and working-class people. As we have noted elsewhere there is now an increasing body of literature which suggests that smoking in disadvantaged and marginalised groups is experienced as having immediate benefits that outweigh long-term health-denying consequences. Health education in this context may be at best ineffective, at worse counterproductive. In relation to their study of smoking amongst low-income pregnant adolescents, for example, Lawson (1994) argues that 'smoking prevention programmes based on an inaccurate understanding of the social context in which smoking occurs can reinforce the use of tobacco among high risk, pregnant adolescents'.

Another example of the limited effectiveness of traditional health education approaches is provided by the study on the prevention of accidents by Sparks, Craven and Worth (1994). This study found that parents operated 'zones of control' based on temporal and spatial dimensions of safety control. These were used in conjunction with parental assumptions about child development. There were social class differences in the ability to use these parentally defined rules which reflected class differences in material resources (presence of a car) and objective hazards in different areas. The authors conclude that there is a need to 'take social class differences into consideration when formulating education and promotional policy in relation to child safety' (Sparks, Craven and Worth, 1994). Similarly, also in relation to childhood accidents Roberts, Bryce and Smith (1993) point out that parents have a good understanding of the causes of accidents, hazards and risk in their own environment and that they are effective most of the time in keeping children safe in unsafe conditions. In this context they suggest that 'educating' parents about childhood accidents is not cost-effective. Whilst professionals in this study tended to limit their suggestions about prevention to education, parents focused in on tangible and material support such as building appropriate and safe houses or, failing this, making safe the existing housing stock, for instance, through re-wiring.

Kirk and Tinnings study (1994) on the counterproductiveness of physical education lessons for promoting healthy and active lifestyles amongst adolescents provides another example of how health promotion messages may fail to change behaviour. The alienating experience of PE lessons revealed by the qualitative interviews with some young people led the authors to suggest that pedagogic practices in schools required amending if such lessons were to be effective sites for health promotion. As they argue: 'exhortations to lead a more healthy lifestyle only makes sense when it can be shown more or less precisely what this means in any given set of circumstances'. In the case of PE, on the basis of accounts and observation of PE lessons the authors consider the feasibility of adopting health-related activities to be limited due to the nature of schooling, adolescents' interpretations and internalisation of popular physical culture, and the social dynamics of groups of young men and women. They suggest that health education involving physical activity will stand a better chance of success if 'health promoters are able to create circumstances in which individuals can engage in physical tasks without risk to self identity' (p. 622).

## A 'salutogenic' approach to health promotion

Qualitative research suggests that a further reason why messages about adopting healthy behaviours may not be translated into practice is that the focus on negative health is off-putting to certain target groups. In the study by Ritchie, Herscovitch and Norfor (1994) examining perceptions about heart disease and risk factors, the most salient influencing factor in the lives of respondents were considerations of continuing personal well being in the here and now rather than thoughts of getting heart disease in the future. Well being was tied to social affiliation and was viewed in positive terms as something that individuals had control over. Achieving health in contrast was viewed in negative terms as determined by chance and luck rather than individual action. The authors suggest that a salutogenic approach to health promotion, emphasising the link between healthy behaviour and well being, might be more effective than 'the conventional approach of admonishing individuals to instigate changes that are perceived by them as diminishing well being'. In relation to safer sex, the importance of promoting condom sex as good and pleasurable was also the conclusion of an Australian study examining the use of condoms in heterosexual people (Browne and Minichiello, 1994).

Though research has often reported so-called 'negative' definitions of health amongst some lay groups, this may in fact be an artefact of the traditional methodology used in epidemiology and health surveys. In their study of people's images of health, for instance, d'Houtard and Field (1984) collected data from open-ended questions. They found in analysing the data that whilst at first sight (on a simple numerical count) a negative definition of health predominated – i.e. not to be sick – by combining similar themes together to create new categories (for example, the joy of life, life without constraint, to benefit from life, to live as long as possible and to be involved in outdoor life as much as possible), the balance tipped in favour of a salutogenic configuration.

A salutogenic approach to health promotion may be more appropriate in some contexts than others, and there is also evidence that this may be class related. The d'Houtard and Field study (1984), for example, indicated a clear class gradient in salutogenic perceptions of health. Whilst the manual class group were found to express more 'negative' imagery, positive notions of health fitted more with middle-class norms, values and social roles.

## Lay people as a health promotion resource

Qualitative research sheds light on the considerable potential for lay people to act as a resource in health promotion. As we discussed earlier, from a professional health promotion perspective many aspects of lifestyles and modes of behaviour would be considered to be harmful. However, some aspects of lay risk assessment and reduction are, as we have seen, positive and therefore warrant inclusion in health promotion strategies. To an extent this is already happening in the area of HIV prevention, but is less prevalent in other areas of health promotion.

A further and perhaps more important reason for considering lay people as a resource for health promotion is indicated by work which suggests that an understanding of the precise details of people's lifestyles is crucial to developing effective strategies for addressing variations in health and targeting interventions which are both meaningful and relevant. Social networks and rules which underpin the everyday 'health-damaging' lifestyles of 'at-risk' health groups have been viewed by some researchers as an important health promoting resource. For example, functional and reciprocal relations have been identified as underlying the networks of injectors of illicit drugs. As Power and colleagues point out:

> informal peer education and health advocacy is a common occurrence among drug-user networks often promoted by key opinion leaders and high status individuals such as drug-dealers. This largely untapped resource should be a main component of community-based HIV prevention strategies (Power et al., 1995, p. 566).

This study points to the usefulness of ethnographic studies in pin-pointing foci for effective interventions. Similarly in the context of demonstrating that people account for health and illness and related behaviour in terms of their comprehension of their social circumstances and obligations, Backett and Davison (1995) argue that effective health promotion strategies should work with everyday cultural norms about social organisation in order to understand the components of acceptable health-relevant behaviour. Understanding the everyday social behaviour of individuals is also likely to contribute to the development of more appropriate and acceptable interventions to promote health.

A number of the qualitative studies reviewed also suggest that lay people may have knowledge about risks to health which is not readily accessible to professionals. Living in poor material circumstances, for example, appears to have given women detailed knowledge of local hazards in relation to child accidents which would be invaluable in planning accident reduction initiatives. Similarly, 'local understandings' are an important dimension in understanding the epidemiological nature of environmental pollution (Phillimore and Moffatt, 1994).

The hidden role lay people have always played in promoting health and preventing ill health is illustrated by the historical analysis undertaken by Carol Thomas (1995). She demonstrates 'the unrecognised historical contribution made by domestic labourers to the improvement in the health status of the population in industrial Britain'. Using a variety of historical documents Thomas demonstrates how the labour undertaken by women in their roles as mothers and housewives has been a key factor in constructing a domestic environment which has made an (officially unrecognised) contribution to falling mortality rates in the late nineteenth and early twentieth century.

A further argument for placing greater emphasis on the potential of lay people as a resource in health promotion relates to the low priority and negative perception that some professionals with responsibility for health promotion may hold about this role. A qualitative study of GPs' perceptions of coronary heart disease prevention is instructive in this regard (Williams and Calnan, 1994). The themes which emerged from the personal accounts of 40 GPs suggested that the notion of prevention was considered to be problematic and that they wished to have limited personal involvement in such activities. They considered that health promotion was, 'a dull, boring and tedious activity', detracted from curative medicine, and was shot through with uncertainties about the identification of risk and its management, and they questioned its effectiveness in changing behaviour. Further themes related to the fact that health promotion was considered a moral intrusion and inflated patients' anxiety levels needlessly. The last two themes reinforce the argument for an approach which pays greater attention to the acceptability and appropriateness of attempts to influence people's behaviour.

## *The need for more qualitative research*

The questions posed by attempts to link habits and orientations to life expectancy and health status has meant that much of the research into the social patterning of health, illness and death undertaken so far has been quantitative. However, there is a rapidly growing body of research relevant to this field which uses qualitative methods alone or in combination, and there is a vociferous critique of the tyranny within health research of 'risk epidemiology' (Dean, 1994). To date much of the relevant qualitative research has been concerned to understand the meanings people attached to particular actions or to the experience of health and illness, death and dying. More qualitative research is needed to explore the social distribution of the context and processes with which health-related actions are shaped. Most importantly, there is a role for qualitative research in illuminating further the vital link between human agency and the structural context of people's lives.

It is apparent from our review, that some areas of risky health behaviour have received more attention than others. Since the mid-1980s, work on HIV disease and AIDS has dominated health research on risk both in qualitative and quantitative studies. This intense focus on HIV/AIDS within the qualitative literature has had the advantage of enabling a detailed examination of discrete groups to take place in which the detailed complexities of lay health knowledge and relationship to individual and group action have been made more visible.

The amount and nature of the work undertaken in the field of HIV/AIDS highlight two issues which have importance for establishing a research and development strategy for health promotion directed at reducing variations in health. First, this illustrates the considerable potential for work exploring the micro processes associated with individual behaviours to begin to flesh out the bare bones provided by macro studies of variations in health status. It can reveal mediating factors between macro structures and processes and individuals' behaviour and the way in which risk factors are perceived by different lay groups and professionals. Existing qualitative research on HIV/AIDS also highlights the dearth of information about other areas of lifestyle/health behaviour.

# Variations in health and health promotion: key messages from qualitative research

The qualitative research reviewed in this report points to a number of key issues which need to be addressed to increase the effectiveness of health promotion strategies and practices in the context of variations in health.

1. The most important message to emerge from this review is that individual behaviour relevant to health is embedded and formed by aspects of everyday life, social relationships, and material resources. Specific health-related behaviours are the product of the interaction between individuals and social structures, and health promotion strategies aiming to reduce variations in health must address the complexity and diversity inherent in this model.

2. Qualitative research has subjected many of the concepts central to existing health promotion strategies to detailed scrutiny. These include notions of 'lifestyle', 'healthy behaviour', 'risk' and 'empowerment'. The review has suggested that there can be fundamental problems in applying these concepts at the individual or locality level without reference to a detailed understanding of local social and material environments. There is, therefore, a need for an audit of the key concepts which inform the development of health promotion strategies for variations in health.

3. The review has highlighted significant areas of convergence between professional and lay views of health and behaviour. It is important that those involved in health promotion are aware of areas of consensus with regard to values and knowledge (of prominent risk factors, for instance) in order to reinforce messages to which people will be receptive.

4. The review has also highlighted areas of divergence between professional and lay groups. The greatest differences may relate to the assessment of risk. In some instances, non-action or a different action to that proposed by health promoters may be seen as the most rational action by lay people. Fatalism, in some situations, is better construed as a realistic appraisal of the potential for individual control rather than an intrapersonal quality associated with an external locus of control. Behaviours construed within health promotion as

'negative' may be viewed by lay people as pleasurable parts of everyday life and/or essential to maintaining a sense of wellbeing and control. Alternatively, some activities portrayed as 'positive' within health promotion, may have negative effects for key groups. In this context, to construe particular individual behaviours as simplistically 'negative' or 'positive' in health terms is unlikely to lead to change.

5. The review suggests that lay experiences may make an important contribution to the knowledge base for health promotion. In some of the studies reviewed lay people had identified 'new' risk factors worthy of consideration within health promotion, and they had strongly held views about appropriate ways of intervening to promote health. Similarly, coping mechanisms, such as 'disengagement', which are used and valued by lay people may need to be given greater recognition within health promotion.

6. Much of the research into subjective meanings and health behaviour points strongly to the need for a more prominent 'environmental' focus to health promotion, rather than a narrow focus on individual behavioural change. A greater explicit recognition within health promotion policy and practice of the importance of context for behaviour and of environmental barriers to change (including for example, poverty, poor housing, social exclusion and powerlessness) may promote a more constructive partnership with lay groups, particularly those which are marginalised and disadvantaged.

7. Qualitative research in the HIV/AIDS field indicates the potential of a close understanding of the social and material context for individual behaviour to inform effective health promotion interventions. This level of understanding is lacking in many areas relevant to health promotion. More qualitative research is therefore needed. However, change in policy and practice does not need to await the results of research. Rather, as illustrated by some of the work reviewed, research into context and meanings can and should run alongside and shape practical health promotion initiatives. In particular there is a need for further qualitative research exploring social variations in the process which mediates between macro structures and individual behaviour and the way in which risk factors are perceived amongst different lay groups and professionals.

# PART II:
# Setting standards for qualitative research: The development of markers

# Markers for the evaluation of qualitative research

> If we are to understand the detailed means through which human beings engage in meaningful action and create a world of their own or one that is shared with others we must acknowledge that insufficient attention has been devoted to evolving criteria for assessing the general quality and rigor of interpretive research (Altheide and Johnson, 1994).

The methodology for conducting literature reviews has developed considerably in recent years. Reviews of quantitative research, particularly RCTs, have developed a hierarchy of evidence which distinguishes between study designs according to their susceptibility to bias (Woolfe *et al.*, 1993). These hierarchies are not applicable to qualitative research but different criteria can and should be applied.

There are three specific reasons why the development of qualitative markers has become more urgent in recent times. First, as systematic criteria for the assessment of quantitative methods such as the randomised controlled trial (RCT) have been developed, qualitative methods are in danger of being perceived as the poor relation in health services research (HSR): a source of interesting anecdotes, but not to be treated seriously as science. To an extent the arguments to be made for a set of markers for qualitative research are similar to the arguments which have been made for criteria for the systematic review of randomised control trials. If 'evidence-based' practice is to extend beyond the RCT, valuable as it is, then research pertaining to all aspects of health services needs criteria against which to judge quality. Health-care providers, researchers and policymakers are inundated with large amounts of information and need to be discriminating. This is particularly the case with qualitative research, as the principles involved seem less familiar to those working in the health field. Additionally as Mulrow (1994) has pointed out, a set of criteria for systematic reviewing is necessary for rational decision-making and the integration of existing information. This is no less applicable to qualitative than it is to quantitative research.

Secondly, within the health services research field, beyond the boundaries of medical sociology, the practice of qualitative research is underdeveloped and often lacks methodological and theoretical inspiration. As qualitative methods and techniques become used more widely outside the disciplines in which they were first developed, there is a danger that the techniques will become divorced from the theoretical assumptions supporting their use. Thirdly, there are calls from qualitative researchers themselves for renewed criteria for assessing interpretive validity in qualitative research. In particular there have been concerns expressed about the appropriate representation of the actions and accounts given by respondents and calls for accountability for the interpretations made by investigators (Altheide and Johnson, 1994). These concerns are relevant to social science research in applied fields such as health services research.

# Criteria for assessing the validity of qualitative research from within the social sciences

Social scientists have flagged up a number of different ways in which qualitative research can be assessed and good interpretation ensured (Hammersley, 1992; Denzin and Lincoln, 1994). The position taken here views qualitative research as a distinct paradigm requiring a different approach to quality assessment to that of the existing literature on systematic review methodology. Denzin and Lincoln (1994, p. 480) have argued for efforts to be deployed in the construction of a set of validity criteria which 'would flow from the qualitative project, stressing subjectivity, emotionality, feeling and other anti-foundational factors'. It is arguably the case that, within the health field, the most important contribution qualitative research can and should make is in illuminating the subjective meaning of experiences and behaviour and exploring the link between knowledge, action and wider social and economic circumstances. This contribution is the focus of the literature review contained in Part I of this report. Central to this position is the assumption that lay people and patients are experts who are skilled, knowledgeable and trained about health and illness and that there is much to learn from tapping into that expertise. This position does not claim that lay people are always 'right' (just as professionals are not always right) but underpinning lay knowledge and action there is a logic and system that must be understood if there is to be meaningful dialogue and change.

Given this focus our particular concern has been to develop a framework for judging the quality of research aiming to increase understanding of the relationship between knowledge and behaviour (whether amongst 'lay' or professional groups). But devising one set of markers does not, of course, preclude the development of a range of different sets of qualitative research markers to judge. Qualitative research methods are used in the furtherance of other aims and in such cases a different framework with different criteria will be appropriate. There can be considerable overlap between these sets of markers as to what constitutes 'good' qualitative research. However, a plurality of criteria is both inevitable and desirable in order to fit the multiple frames of reference which are to be found in HSR.

Many of the problems faced in evaluating the use of qualitative research methods in the literature are the same as for quantitative methods. For example, reports, articles, and books rarely provide enough detail of the methods used for an adequate judgement to be made about the quality of the study being reported. However, there are characteristics of qualitative research which make the development of assessment markers more complex than is the case with quantitative methods. These can be grouped under three headings: epistemology, methodology, and research practice.

## Epistemology

All researchers, whatever their methodological preference, would agree that 'explanatory power' is an important gold standard for evaluation of any piece of research, and that explanation is 'better than' description. However, there are differences over the way these terms are defined and applied to particular pieces of work. Qualitative research may be too easily dismissed as 'descriptive' by those who misunderstand the form and content of explanation in the social sciences, where the distinction between theory and description is not a simple one. Whilst description may be seen as a resource which is able to provide 'information about' a particular topic it may also be a basis for analytic inquiry (Stanley, 1990). Moreover, the goal in qualitative research may be more to do with interpreting what something *means,* than in explaining why it happened. However, the process of describing in detail the circumstances surrounding an event or an experience, and of exploring people's perceptions of, and responses to, those circumstances in the situation in which those circumstances occur, may itself constitute the grounds for 'explanation'. To make use of Weber's distinction, in qualitative research the point of the explanation is not in the first instance adequacy at the *level* of cause, as it is for example in traditional experimental design, but adequacy at the level of *meaning.* An explanation that is meaningful may then help us to understand why something has happened or is the way it is.

## Methodology

One of the most obvious differences between qualitative and quantitative research is the apparent absence of standardised procedures (or codes) to follow when using particular qualitative methods. For example, judgements about the equation of sample size and statistical significance and power, which routinely inform our evaluation of quantitative studies, have no equivalent in qualitative studies (although there are particular types of sampling which will influence whether the criteria of adequacy at the level of subjective meaning are met). There is no simple checklist of procedures which can provide an obvious picture of the worth of a particular piece of research. In the context of attention to 'meaning' qualitative methods need to be able to be responsive to circumstances as they exist, rather than attempt to create a situation in which the variables of interest can be controlled and their relationships examined. For this reason, the hallmark of good qualitative methodology is its flexibility rather than its standardisation. The point of the methodology is not that it can be applied and compared across all other similarly controlled situations, but that it can be modified and be responsive to the particularities of situations as they arise in real-life social settings.

## *Research practice*

The uncodified nature of much qualitative analysis poses another problem for anyone wishing to set up a methodological marking system for qualitative studies. In contrast to most quantitative studies, the phases of the research process – sampling, data collection, data analysis and interpretation – are not separate. Sampling, for example, is interdependent with data collection, data collection overlaps with data analysis, and the movement from analysis to interpretation is not clear cut.

# Developing markers: A preliminary framework

It is against this background that we have begun to develop markers against which qualitative research can be assessed.

Our aim has been to use them as the basis for exploring how standards or criteria might be applied in literature reviews of qualitative research, rather than to apply them formally to all the work we have reviewed for this report. The markers being developed relate to three key areas:

(i)   The nature of the knowledge generated by research

(ii)  The place of quantification

(iii) Validity and adequacy.

## The knowledge question: the primary marker

Research methods are more than a set of techniques, and some understanding of the basis on which they claim to produce 'knowledge' is important. From the perspective of this review the most important marker of the calibre of studies using qualitative methods is the extent to which the research adopts a *verstehen* approach to knowledge, illuminating the *subjective* meanings attaching to behaviours and experiences as viewed from *within* a culture, society or group. Within the health field (and indeed more generally within the academic world) there is widespread misunderstanding of the nature of the knowledge claims that are made for qualitative research and from this flows at least three persistent criticisms:

- that the researcher is subjective and the data biased (this is used to refer both to the nature of the data collected, for example respondents' points of view and the relationship of the research to the data);

- that the data have been collected in an 'uncontrolled' way and cases are selected non-randomly;

- that the cases are too few in number to enable any generalisations to be made.

Lying behind these criticisms is the confusion between statistical (or probabilistic) and logical (or theoretical) generalisation. The issue from an interpretist perspective is not whether the cases or individuals are 'representative' of a population but rather whether the themes emerging from the analysis connect with existing bodies of theoretical knowledge or generate new understanding.

## Quantification: a superficial marker

Researchers using qualitative methods in the 1960s may have adopted a certain vagueness as a deliberate policy — a means of down-playing the importance of quantification and demarcating the separation of qualitative from quantitative studies. However more recent commentators have taken a different tack. For an increasing number within the qualitative tradition limited quantification or 'cautious positivism' is an acceptable part of assessing adequacy (Silverman, 1987).

In so far as the value of such limited quantification of qualitative data is accepted, it does provide the basis for the development of *prima facie* criteria for the evaluation of qualitative studies. But there is a danger that such minimal and superficial description of data — at best equivalent to the enumeration of frequencies and the examination of cross-tabulations in survey data — will be mistaken for the analysis itself. In reality, it is only the beginning of a long process of sifting and examining the complex universe of a qualitative data-set.

The introduction of word-processing packages and data-handling packages such as Word for Windows, Nudist and Ethnograph facilitate the handling of qualitative data-sets. They also aid the use of 'cautious positivism'. However, without a thorough appreciation of the properties of the data — particularly the type of knowledge that can be produced by qualitative research — such packages will deliver only an impression of sophistication. Computer-aided analysis does allow for the systematic comparison of themes across and within different population groups — a process which enables the complexity of subjective views and social context to be grasped more fully. However, they are neither necessary nor sufficient for the production of rigorous qualitative analysis. Many examples exist of qualitative studies based on the analysis of handwritten notes which have had continuing influence and undoubted validity across the health field.

## Markers for validity and adequacy

The three objections to qualitative research described above fail to ask the key questions that should underlie the assessment of any piece of research whatever the methods: are the methods used appropriate to the research questions being asked and what data are available, or can be collected, to answer the questions? Once a qualitative approach has been adopted, then validity is assessed in terms of the adequacy and appropriateness of theory and the adequacy and appropriateness of data. It is an assumption of the use of qualitative methods that:

> An account is valid or true if it represents accurately those features of the phenomena that it is intended to describe, explain or theorise. Assumed here, then, is a correspondence theory of truth, but the correspondence involves selective representation rather than reproduction of reality (Hammersley, 1992).

Once the knowledge marker has been applied to qualitative research, there are three further aspects of the research that need to be considered to evaluate whether a study is valid or useful in applied settings: (i) data quality; (ii) theoretical adequacy; and (iii) policy relevance. To some extent these questions are the same whatever the research being evaluated, for there are certain standard questions of logic and method to be considered. However, some questions to be asked of qualitative research will be different from those concerned with quantitative research.

## (i) Data quality

The quality of the data needs to be considered in relation to a number of key questions:*

- What have the data been collected for?

- Is the process by which individuals or cases were 'selected' adequately described?

- Is the manner in which questions have been asked or observations made adequately specified? (For example has the checklist of topics covered in a semi-structured interview been described.)

- What is the context in which the data have been collected and how did the researcher 'negotiate' it?

- Does the research use and compare different sources of data about the same issue where that is appropriate? (This is not just to ensure the accounts coincide, as in triangulation, but helps illuminate different facets of the aspects of reality under investigation.)

*Some of these criteria apply to research generally and relate to the accountability expected from an investigator in writing up the process and results of research.

- Does the researcher explain how the data presented in the report were selected from the larger data-set?

- Are the limitations of the data discussed in relation to the questions being asked?

- Are the data being presented as 'factual' reports or as subjective perceptions and experiences?

It is important to recognise that data are not 'pure'. As Plummer has noted (1983) there is a continuum of contamination in both the collection and the presentation of the data. In any research report, it is necessary to examine the way in which the data have been shaped by the researchers' questions or observations, and used in the context of a particular set of arguments. Given the involvement of the researcher in the research process, the question is not whether or not the data are biased, but to what extent the researcher has made transparent the processes by which they have been collected, analysed, and presented. Qualitative research treats all data as the product of interaction. In contrast to the guiding assumption of the experiment, it is neither possible nor desirable to try and eliminate the researcher's influence on the situation.

## (ii) Theoretical adequacy

Data have no meaning in themselves. The next set of questions concern the way in which researchers present the meaning and significance of the data that have been collected. In relation to qualitative research we are principally concerned with interpretive validity. Recently this has been conceived of as a matter of 'reflexive accounting' (Altheide and Johnson, 1994). This necessitates the researcher clearly specifiying 'the interactions which have occurred among themselves, their methodologies and the settings and actors studied' (Denzin and Lincoln, 1994, p. 481). Clearly the limits to this will be determined by the amount of space permitted for writing up published research in journals.

Validity is about the interpretations placed upon the data in relation to the source and form of the data themselves. In other words, consideration of the validity of a piece of work is a consideration of its overall adequacy, plausibility, and sense-making qualities. In qualitative research the question of the 'adequacy' of data is central. A piece of research that relates only to itself – its own data, context, or research topic – is of value in theoretical terms, and may exhibit considerable policy relevance, and inform practical and policy initiatives. However, a generic conceptual framework, one that identified patterns that apply to a wider variety of social phenomena, is likely to be of even more value in health research. Questions to be asked to assess the theoretical adequacy of qualitative research would include the following:

- Is the relationship between the data and the original theoretical argument clearly articulated?

- Does the researcher indicate the links between the data presented and his or her own commentary on what the data contain?

- How does the research move from a description of the data, through quotation or examples, to an analysis and interpretation of the meaning and significance of it?★

- What claims are being made for the generalisability of the findings to other bodies of knowledge or to other populations or groups?†

- Are the data presented to provide evidence both for and against the argument being made or the theory being elaborated?

- Are paradoxes, contradictions or inconsistencies in the data properly explained?

- Do the data and the theoretical discussion together 'make sense' in terms of what is known from other studies?

- Are the findings transferrable to other contexts?

- Is the context within which the study takes place made explicit?

Some of these criteria relate to the adequacy of the process: the clarity of the description, the logic of the analysis, and the imagination in the interpretation. Others are about the qualities of what is produced: the coherence, the fairness and honesty, the generalisability, and the transferability. The popularity of multi-site samples as a source of comparison and contrasts, has increased but limited funding means concentration on single case studies. The validity of single case studies is predicated on the notion of context. Because the way in which a case study fits into a body of theory or other findings is important, the research report should provide background information sufficient to make these judgements.

★In a full report one would expect to find some evidence of the constant comparative method whereby the researcher uses comparative analysis to look for statements and indices of behaviour that occur over time and in a range of periods during the study. What can be provided for a journal article is more limited but one could reasonably expect the researcher to refer to any major tensions or conflict in the data for example between private and public accounts.

† Whilst, as we discuss below, qualitative research can to an extent be generalised to different settings, claims should not be overstated. Qualitative researchers should not be aiming for traditional generalisability which may limit the questions of meaning and interpretation of a specific 'case study'.

Criticisms of the scope for representativeness and generalisability of qualitative research made by those more familiar with RCTs or statistical surveys are based upon a narrow and singular view of the nature of generalisation. For example, Goffman's analysis of the mental hospital as a total institution and the dehumanising processes such hospitals gave rise to, was carried out in an American context based on his own participant observation of a single ward (Goffman, 1963). Nonetheless, in spite of its apparent idiosyncracies, studies carried out later, using a variety of different research designs, indicate that generalising about total institutions on the basis of Goffman's study was wholly valid. Moreover, settings do not have to be *typical* for generalisations to be made. The general relevance may derive from their atypicality. Details about time and place are also important, as are the populations that generalisations might be made to (for example, views of a mainly female population might not be those of men).

## (iii) Policy relevance

The applicability of any criteria for judging research quality will vary according to the intended purpose of the research. Some view the purpose of qualitative research as essentially descriptive and thus 'adequacy', they argue, should be based on the richness of the picture that such research produces. Similarly, where policy is the main focus, data should address the issues of concern to the different 'stakeholders' involved with that policy. As Hammersley (1992) points out, qualitative research reports need to contain an assessment of the whole range of relevant studies in an area in order to be policy relevant. It is also important to ask how relevant the research is in terms of the topic being investigated, its contribution to the literature and its relevance to practitioners and policymakers. Finally, it is important to ask whether overall the claims being made in the report are plausible and credible given what we know about the methods, theory, data collection, analysis and context. Qualitative research is generally accepted as more accessible to potential user groups than some quantitative research. Therefore, a further marker might be the extent to which qualitative research empowers key groups using or participating in health services.

# Applying the markers

In the literature review reported here, we have considered the way in which the markers discussed above might be used to assess the research reported. We did not do this systematically, as our aim was to consider further refinement of the markers. However, using 'knowledge' which gives primacy to the subjective meaning of lay populations as our principal marker, together with the three markers for assessing validity and adequacy (data quality, theoretical adequacy and policy relevance), a number of observations can be made about some of the papers we selected for review.

## The categorisation of data and their impact on description

The way in which data categorisation can affect the 'meaning' provided by respondents is illustrated by two studies. The overlap between medical and lay conceptualisations of illness in the accounts of patients consulting primary care services in Finland was explored in an article by Punamaki and Kokko (1995). The authors reported that the most common explanation for patient consultation related to infectious, toxic and noxious agents and constitutional defects in the body. However, whilst the questions asked were open-ended, the way in which questions and topics were introduced suggests that the themes may have been more medically than lay framed. The following description of the research process illustrates the point: the patients' explanations of illness were drawn from the discussion around the following question and topics: 'What is your own diagnosis? What is your own idea of why you are ill now? What causes the illness and what factors are associated with your recovery?'

In contrast, the work of d'Houtard and Field (1984) which attempted to ascertain lay imagery of health and illness, appears to be more sensitive to the wording of questions as indicated by this comment from the methods section:

> . . . our open-ended question came toward the end of the health examination after three open-ended questions concerning the individual's motivation for coming to the examination, his impression and his suggestions. It was formulated as follows: What is according to you the best definition of health? At first such a formulation has the inconvenience of appearing rather abstract. One could have, for example, preferred to ask 'What is health?' However the second formulation which is certainly more concrete, might have in our

opinion, the risk of orientating informants toward less varied, more stereo-typed, even tautological responses of the type 'to feel well'.

## Studies using quantitative and qualitative research methods

A significant number of articles claimed to use both qualitative and quantitative research methods. Overall we found that where both methods were used primacy was usually given to quantitative analysis. This tended to affect the richness and calibre of the reported qualitative findings. Some papers initially claiming to use qualitative and quantitative approaches were on closer scrutiny found not to present any qualitative findings. At other times the use of qualitative data was confined to pre-empirical testing for a quantitative project. An example of this is the study by Gottlieb *et al.* (1992) which evaluated the implementation of a work-place smoking policy. In this study qualitative data in the form of written comments from respondents, group interviews with smokers and non-smokers and individual interviews with supervisors were used to elucidate the quantitative findings and to identify the key themes which appeared to have the strongest influence on expected and unexpected outcomes of the smoking policy. However in using the qualitative data simply to construct key variables and illustrate quantitative findings, the subjective meaning of respondents was lost.

A further example of the problems of ensuring qualitative adequacy in the report-ing of mixed method studies is a study which examined the role of community pharmacists in health promotion. Qualitative data were collected as part of a larger survey including 148 interviews with community pharmacists, observation and ethnographic field notes. However, these were not used to address specific research questions but rather simply to illuminate quantitative findings. In terms of links to theory the researchers relied on a simple listing of quotes in categories based on quantitative analysis. With regard to methods there was little detail provided on data collection methods, no information on analysis and no way of assessing data quality even though the paper claimed to report 'mainly on the qualitative material'. In terms of its policy relevance, policy links were established but there was an absence of theorising which limited the opportunity to explore important policy questions, for example, pharmacists' perception of customers.

An exception to the tendency to give primacy to quantitative elements in mixed method studies was an article by Sparks, Craven and Worth (1994) on differences in the perceptions of childhood safety. Here quantitative data on the rate of accidents between localities were used as a backdrop against which to conduct depth interviews with parents in areas with high and low accident rates. This study was illuminating in terms of locating the lay assessment of risk in relation to context, agency and structure.

## *Interpretive validity*

The major issue here is whether or not the meaning and viewpoint of research subjects are given due weight compared to researchers' interpretations. There were a number of studies identified in the review in which the meaning of the investigator or those representing official health voices were prioritised in a context in which, on the face of things, the views of lay people were being sought. This was the case in a study which examined smoking amongst low-income pregnant adolescents where the analysis was concerned with professional interpretations, rather than the meaning of smoking for adolescents (Wearing, Wearing and Kelly, 1994). The notion of role model, for example, was used as a reference point for the authors: 'for these youths, identity establishment was particularly difficult due to the lack of positive role models'. In contrast two other studies about smoking were grounded in lay constructs and meaning. Here explanations about smoking behaviour centred around the perceived benefits and costs from the respondents' perspectives (Lawson, 1994; Graham, 1987). Similarly, the use of the term 'defensive denial' to describe women's means of coping with incontinence (Ashworth and Hagan, 1993) is an example of a psycho-dynamically informed construct derived from the researchers, rather than respondents interpretations.

The depth of analysis also varied considerably across studies. Some studies used data as a descriptive resource with little attempt at interpretation or grounded theorising. Other studies provided grounded accounts which provided insights into both meaning and 'causal' processes. For example in the work on HIV by Koniak–Griffin *et al.* (1994) the emphasis appeared to be on describing and categorising the range and types of risky behaviour reported by respondents. In contrast the work of McKeganey, Barnard and Bloor (1990) centred on sexual practices which encompassed not only individual behaviour but dyadic behaviour and considered the context for sexual activity. This wider analytic view allowed greater understanding of the issue under investigation.

A final example of the relevance of different interpretive stances is provided from the literature on diet. For Brug *et al.* (1995) the focus was on the awareness or otherwise of health promotion messages about food amongst respondents. In contrast, other research explored the ways in which views and practices about food and eating were not necessarily orientated towards a health agenda but were deeply embedded in everyday practices linked to pleasure, ritual and everyday norms, beliefs and values (Calnan and Williams 1987).

# Concluding comment

Our preliminary attempts at devising and applying a set of markers suggest that there is diversity in the quality of published qualitative research in the field of health behaviour. Despite this diversity most studies were adequate as measured by one of our three markers. However, the studies which were able to meet the criteria of adequacy at the level of knowledge, subjective meaning and context were far fewer. Whilst there is no good reason to exclude qualitative studies which do not meet quality standards on all three markers, those studies which meet the requirements of interpretative validity should be given more weight in reviews than those that do not.

# PART III:
# Technical report

# Introduction: Methodological developments

As we have already noted, the methodology for conducting literature reviews has developed considerably in recent years. Sheldon and his colleagues at York University's Centre for Reviews and Dissemination, have produced a framework which is now widely used for conducting systematic reviews (1993). Whilst, as we have already discussed, the approach to assessing the quality of research proposed by Sheldon *et al.* is not appropriate for a review of qualitative research, other elements of their review framework could be followed.

# The search: The research question and methods

## The research question

The primary question addressed by the review was: what insights can be gained from qualitative research regarding the factors that constrain and/or facilitate changes in behaviour which would be conducive to promoting health and reducing ill health. A secondary question concerned the extent to which this research illuminated the relationship between individual behaviour/action and social variations in the experience of health, illness and death.

For the purposes of the review variations in health status of primary interest were those associated with differences in socio-economic status, gender, ethnicity, age or geographical region. Health issues of primary concern were related to the Health of the Nation key areas: CHD/stroke, cancer and smoking, mental health, sexual health and AIDS/HIV, and accidents, as well as the risk factors of smoking, diet and exercise. Studies were also analysed in relation to the key concepts of risk, prevention, lifestyle, control, and social support.

## The review methods

### Inclusion and exclusion criteria

To be included in the review, reports of research had to satisfy criteria of relevance and design.

(i)   Relevance – Studies which aimed to illuminate factors shaping health-related behaviour were included. These could be studies looking at behaviour in the relevant areas of health behaviour listed above or studies which did not specifically consider individual behaviour but illuminated other relevant issues such as those referred to above, for example, control and social support. Typically, such studies were found in the subject areas of medical sociology, sociology, social anthropology, psychology, nursing and medicine.

(ii)  Design – This was a review of relevant *qualitative* studies. Research was included which used qualitative methods, for example in-depth unstructured interviews/participant observation or focus groups. The reviewers excluded any research, no matter how relevant the subject matter, which used only quantitative methods, such as the use of structured pre-coded questionnaires (whether administered by post or interviews) or quantitative analysis, such as logistic regression.

There were instances of authors claiming to have used qualitative research methods or analysis, which on closer inspection turned out to be quantitative. Such studies were then discarded.

As noted in Part II, the assessment of standards in qualitative research involves much more than a judgement about the specific method of data collection employed. For example, whilst in-depth interviews may generate potentially rich data about the meanings people attach to a particular experience or behaviour, in the analysis these meanings may be lost and/or overwhelmed by the researchers' interpretations or constructions of the accounts provided. Ideally, whilst an initial inclusion criteria would be the precise method employed, there should be further sifting of studies depending on the 'knowledge' marker and markers for validity and adequacy discussed in Part II. In the event, as we have noted, these were not applied systematically for all the studies identified and included in the review. Our marker framework was not sufficiently well developed to permit this in the time available.

Studies in the English language relating to any country were considered.

## Identifying the relevant literature

The relevant literature was identified through discussions between members of the qualitative review team and with members of the wider consortia team conducting other elements of the HEA-funded review of research on social variations in health. In addition we also approached other experts in the field.

## The search strategy

The search strategy used was in two parts. First, academic journals were manually scrutinised. Second, the computer database, Social Science Citation Index, was systematically searched using key terms. The subject area of the review, i.e. health and health behaviour, crosses the boundaries of many disciplines and a straightforward search of particular academic journals would not have given sufficient coverage. A combination of computerised and manual searching methods was therefore found to be most suitable.

(i)   An initial manual search was undertaken of selected volumes of academic journals in the subject area of medical sociology and related subject areas of medicine, psychology, nursing and sociology. From these subject areas a number of journals were selected on the basis of their having produced the greatest number of relevant studies, namely: *Social Science and Medicine, Sociology of Health and Illness,* and the *Journal of Health and Social Behaviour.* Detailed searches were then made of the contents pages of these selected journals in the libraries of Manchester University and Salford University for the years 1980–95. Where this resulted in the identification of studies which appeared to be relevant, copies were obtained.

(ii)  Using the product of the manual search and general knowledge of the field, search terms were identified by the four members of the review team and were then used to identify potentially relevant studies from the Social Science Citation Index. From initial searching it appeared that the vast majority of studies relevant to the review had been published between 1990 and 1995: these dates were therefore selected for the search. Moreover, because the search terms used could potentially yield thousands of references, and a time limit had to be set for the search, this was felt to be a logical step. The manual search had in any event identified key studies from earlier periods. On the basis of the search terms used several thousand references were obtained. Considerable time and effort was then put into identifying studies that were relevant to this particular review using the inclusion criteria discussed above. Whenever possible, the full report or article was then obtained, though this was subject to the limitations of the timescale of the review and to cost.

Three sets of terms were used to search the Social Science Citation Index:

(i)   food, diet, eating, prevention, lifestyle, smoking, accident

(ii)  control, social support, risk

(iii) qualitative, interpretive, subjective, interview.

The final aspect of the search strategy retrieved papers which included headings or text words either in their title or abstract to indicate that they:

(a)   reported a research study

(b)   described an appropriate (qualitative) design and analysis

(c)   mentioned one or more of the factors associated with variations in health and health behaviour defined in the above.

## Inclusion and data extraction

Taking the full articles identified through the manual search and the abstracts from the computer database search, one reviewer applied the crude inclusion criteria discussed above and their decisions were cross-checked by another member of the review team. As already noted, we would have wished at this stage to subject full reports on all of the included studies to further critical review using the markers we have been developing to assess the 'quality' of qualitative research. The particular concern would have been to identify research concerned not simply with using one of a range of qualitative methods but rather with using these methods to illuminate the subjective meanings attaching to health, illness and health behaviour amongst lay groups. However, we were only able to apply our marker framework to a limited number of studies, as discussed in Part II of this report. Additionally, whilst attempts were made to obtain full copies of all included articles this was not always possible. For all of the articles finally included in the reviews, core information was collated on the aims of the study, the methods employed and key points emerging from the analysis. These are summarised in Tables 1–7 and full references are given in the Bibliography. The tables cover research focusing on: smoking, accidents, diet, risk, control, social support and prevention and lifestyle.

# Tables of studies for Health of the Nation areas: smoking, accidents, diet

## Table 1 Smoking

| Author(s) | Aims | Methods | Key points |
|---|---|---|---|
| **Beardall and Edwards (1995)** | To identify cultural and social determinants of smoking behaviour. | Qualitative: Unstructured interviews with 10 immigrant informants in Ontario Canada. | Smoking accepted in many groups. Strong gender differences apparent. Knowledge of health problems in relation to smoking and environmental tobacco smoke poor. Causes of smoking vary according to ethnic group. |
| **Casey *et al.* (1993)** | To examine alcoholism within a family context. | Quantitative: Questionnaire of 91 male participants in residential treatment programmes aged between 26 and 63 in USA. Qualitative: Face-to-face unstructured interviews with their wives/partners. | Majority of working wives reported minimal negative impact of their husband's drinking on all areas of their work functioning. Apparent that alcoholism in family member intrudes into workplace, e.g. leads to wives changing jobs and absenteeism. |
| **Gottlieb *et al.* (1992)** | To investigate the implementation of a restrictive smoking policy in decentralised worksites. | Quantitative: 3 cross-sectional surveys of employees and supervisors in USA before and after implementation of restrictive smoking. Qualitative: Written comments on surveys; focus groups; unstructured interviews. | Important characteristics *re* concept, context and process were degree of policy restrictiveness; job type; participation in formulation and implementation; support for enforcers. Bans easier to enforce than restrictions. |
| **Wearing, Wearing and Kelly (1994)** | To examine the role of smoking in the formation of identity for adolescent girls. | Qualitative: Semi-structured interviews with adolescent girls in Australia, UK, USA. | Adventurous leisure which provides physical, mental and emotional challenge and satisfaction can provide a basis for resisting gender stereotypes and provide alternatives to smoking. |

**Table 2 Accidents**

| Author(s) | Aims | Methods | Key points |
|---|---|---|---|
| **Sparks, Craven and Worth (1994)** | To aid the development of appropriate policies to reduce the accident mortality rate for children under 15. | Qualitative: Collection of accident data for 0- to 16-year-olds using Huddersfield Royal Infirmary A and E Department UK. Qualitative: In-depth interviews with parents from areas with high ($n = 14$) and parents from areas with low child accident rate ($n = 16$). | Differences in parental perceptions on safety and beliefs between areas. Social class differences in effective use of safety rules developed by parents. |
| **Rice *et al.* (1994)** | To study child accidents and the maintenance of safety in the family. | Qualitative: group interviews; survey of families with child under 14; case studies of accident prevention strategies. | Research project and parents' action group provide useful local safety data and explore ways of making communities safer for children. Social context an important issue. |
| **Roberts, Bryce and Smith (1993)** | To gauge responsibility for the maintenance of child safety. | Qualitative: Unstructured interviews with parents and professionals. | Parents committed to responsibility for child safety. Professionals differed from parents as rarely linked safety to outside agencies. |
| **Pearson *et al.* (1993)** | To assess women's use of primary health care services. | Qualitative: Semi-structured interviews. | Decision-making process strongly influenced by material resources, social relationships and past practical support. |
| **Mayall (1993)** | To discuss the division of of labour in health care between children, parents and teachers, focusing on children as a social group. | Qualitative: Observation, informal discussion with teachers and children; semi-structured interviews with children. | The social and emotional context of the home and the school, and children's own social worlds, structures of children's health care activities and experience. |

## Table 3 Diet

| Author(s) | Aims | Methods | Key points |
|---|---|---|---|
| **Anderson (1987)** | To assess influences on daily management (diet, exercise, medication, blood testing) of diabetes by Euro-Canadian and Chinese-Canadian women. | Qualitative: In-depth interviews with 196 women. | Diabetes management: not reducible to ethnicity; multifaceted: dependent on life circumstances, e.g. access to resources. |
| **Brug et al. (1995)** | To obtain information about motivations for eating fruit and vegetables. | Qualitative: Focus group interviews with 7 men and 22 women, aged 24–66 in the Netherlands. | Identified 6 issues: satisfaction, especially taste; perceived health consequences; social influences; skills and barriers; habit; lack of awareness of health promotion messages. |
| **Davison, Davey and Frankel (1991)** | To assess the appropriateness of current attempts to prevent chronic disease through behavioural change. | Qualitative: Unstructured interviews with 180 randomly sampled people in South Wales. | Lay epidemiology readily accommodates official messages on health behaviour within cultural fields of luck, fate and destiny. A potential barrier to aims of health education. |
| **Holm (1993)** | To gauge the extent dietary practices are compatible with an enjoyable lifestyle. | Quantitative: 8-month dietary intervention study; 30 subjects. Qualitative: Semi-structured interviews with 7 men and 7 women in Denmark. | Participants found recommended diet pleasant to live on, but expected economic and practical difficulties applying it to everyday life. |
| **Lupton and Chapman (1995)** | To investigate media coverage of, and responses of members of lay public to, diet and cholesterol control controversies. | Qualitative: 12 semi-structured focus group discussions (each with 3–5 people) in Sydney, Australia. | Respondents juggled dialectic of health as control and health as release. 'Everything in moderation', regardless of official advice, is a strategy used to cope with confusions over diet. |
| **Tuchman and Levine (1993)** | To analyse New York Jewish attachment to Chinese food by focusing on meanings projected on to food. | Qualitative: unstructured interviews with Jewish respondents, New York, USA. | Patterns of ethnic culture in general are recursive: socially constructed meanings become the raw materials for new cultural creations. |
| **Wood (1995)** | To examine narratives associated with diet. | Qualitative: Semi-structured interviews. | Discussions of food and eating in lay narratives often refer to epicurean enjoyment. |
| **Wight (1993)** | To examine working-class beliefs surrounding diet. | Qualitative: Semi-structured interviews and focus groups. | In the working-class family context positive views are held about the quantity fo food offered at meal times rather than the health-giving properties of that food. |
| **Anderson et al. (1995)** | To assess the effect of cultural and social factors on daily management of diabetes. | Qualitative: In-depth interviews with 196 Euro- and Chinese-Canadian women over 2 years. | Illness management not reducible to ethnicity but to contextual features of a woman's life. |
| **Devine and Olsen (1992)** | To examine the role of women in families in relation to the promotion of nutrition. | Qualitative: In-depth interviews with women at home an in employment outside the home. | Data indicate that social roles influence women's attitudes about personal nutrition; this is modified by women's interpretation of their roles at different life stages. |
| **Woollett et al. (1995)** | To compare ideas and experiences of pregnancy and childbirth. | Quantitative: Structured interview with 143 women. Qualitative: In-depth interviews with 32 women (Asian and non-Asian women), in UK. | Qualitative analysis indicated Asian women subscribed to traditional practice as well as Western maternity care. |

## Tables of studies for key concepts: risk, control, social support, prevention and lifestyle

### Table 4 Risk

| Author(s) | Aims | Methods | Key points |
|---|---|---|---|
| **Pill and Stott (1985b)** | To explore beliefs, attitudes and practices in the area of preventive health behaviour. | Qualitative: Semi-structured interviews with 204 working-class mothers in Wales. | A better understanding of the context of health behaviours leads to a reorientation of stereotyped ideas about health behaviour and class. Fatalism and orientation to lifestyle choices for health are not necessarily contradictory. |
| **Lowy and Ross (1994)** | To report on homosexually active young men's beliefs about sexual risk. | Qualitative: In-depth interviews with 21 gay men, aged 18–39, half of whom were HIV seropositive, in USA. | No close match between risk behaviour as defined by epidemiology and by respondents. 'Folk constructions' of risk influenced by: age, appearance, diction, HIV knowledge. |
| **Chavez et al. (1995)** | To report on perceptions of breast and cervical cancer risk factors. | Qualitative: Unstructured interviews in Spanish or English with 94 Latina and 27 Anglo women; and 30 physicians. | Comparing views about the two cancers revealed that: general themes apply across both cancers; people in multicultural settings integrate beliefs from various sources; the three groups perceive risk factors consistently differently. |
| **Koniak-Griffin et al. (1994)** | To investigate risk-taking behaviours and AIDS knowledge in minority pregnant and parenting adolescents at risk of HIV transmission. | Quantitative: Questionnaire for socio-demographic information and AIDS knowledge test. Qualitative: 7 focus groups with 48 women, aged 12–19, in USA. | Bipolar findings: some women displayed multiple risky behaviour re sex, drugs, alcohol; some none of these. Affected by gender, lifestyle and social context. |
| **McKeganey, Barnard and Bloor (1990)** | To compare female street working prostitutes and male rent boys re HIV risk and practice of safer sex. | Qualitative: Informal street interviews in red-light district of Glasgow with 208 female prostitutes and 24 rent boys. | Rent boys less likely: to be drug users; to insist on safer sexual practices with clients than female prostitutes (perhaps due to rent boy payment after sex). |
| **Lawson (1994)** | To examine the role of smoking in lives of low-income, pregnant adolescents. | Qualitative: In-depth interviews, plus observation of social participation, with 20 primagravidae adolescents, aged 16–18, in USA. | Perceived benefits from smoking outweigh long-term health consequences, e.g. coping with weight gain and abandonment; reducing foetal size and thus birth pain; alternative to parental and peer drug abuse. |
| **Browne and Minichiello (1994)** | To understand the impact of context on decisions about condom use and safer sexual practices. | Qualitative: In-depth interviews with heterosexual partners. | Dialogues about condoms occur at both intrapersonal and interpersonal levels. |
| **Sharma (1992)** | To explore the role of alcohol in people's lives. | Qualitative: Semi-alcohol structured interviews in North Manchester, UK. | Professional groups and lay populations both agree that health problems need to be dealt with holistically. |
| **Brown (1995)** | To assess the contribution of lay people and scientists to human health and scientific endeavour. | Qualitative: Review and qualitative analysis. | Socially constructed popular epidemiology results from a social movement and a new scientific paradigm. |
| **Brown and Masterson-Allen (1994)** | To examine citizen action and participation against health hazards. | Qualitative: Unstructured interviews. | The local community questioned the status of scientific evidence on the link between ill health and exposure to environmental hazards. |

*(handwritten note: Other studies don't mention this.)*

63

| | | | |
|---|---|---|---|
| **Holland et al. (1992)** | To examine private heterosexual encounters. | Qualitative: Semi-structured interviews. | Unsafe sexual practices arise out of the strategic power relationship between male and female partners. |
| **Peterson and Johnstone (1995)** | To assess the inclusion of health promotion as part of drug dependence treatment programmes in prisons. | Qualitative: Thematic analysis of qualitative self-reports by 43 female offenders in Kentucky, USA. | Participants experienced enhancements to self-esteem, health awareness and concerns, healthy lifestyle adoption and relapse prevention skills through health promotion training. |
| **Lengua et al. (1992)** | To elicit inner city parental views about mental health prevention and alcohol and substance abuse amongst children. | Qualitative: Focus group discussions. | Mothers and fathers expressed widely varying views which led the authors to suggest the need to target preventative interventions separately at fathers and mothers. |
| **Balshem et al. (1992)** | To assess sexual activity amongst drug users. | Qualitative: In-depth interviews with 40 drug users and prostitutes in Oregon, USA. | Respondents used conceptions of cleanliness and morality to assess risk in sexual partners central to the dominant culture surrounding them. |
| **Ritchie, Herscovitch and Norfor (1994)** | To gain insight into beliefs of blue collar workers about coronary risk behaviours. | Qualitative: Focus group discussions at 10 worksites in Sydney, Australia. | Achieving well-being seen as ongoing and site of individual control; health, however, seen negatively as avoidance and determined by chance. |
| **Richards (1993)** | To consider social consequences of deployment of genetic testing. | Qualitative: Review. | Widely held lay views about inheritance contrasted with Mendelian theories of geneticists. |
| **Williams and Wood (1986)** | To examine common-sense beliefs among patients about their illnesses. | Qualitative: Semi-structured interviews. | Patients make regular allusions to biographical, social and cultural factors in order to explain health status and behaviour. |
| **Lane (1995)** | To assess women's resistance to childbirth as a site of professionalisation according to its categorisation by medical professionalisation as a site of risk. | Qualitative: Semi-structured interviews with Australian and British women giving birth. | The case of obstetrics shows that the power of the medical lobby is immense, but not impenetrable. |
| **Rogers and Pilgrim (1995)** | To assess main disputes about the benefits and risks of mass childhood immunisation (MCI). | Qualitative: Documentary and semi-structured interviews. | MCI is surfacing as a controversial policy due to emergent cultural emphases about health, e.g. self-responsibility. |
| **Helman (1981)** | To examine dimensions of psychotropic drug use by long-term users. | Qualitative: Semi-structured interviews. | Chronic users' perspectives, symbolic meanings and usage in relation to drugs differed according to their use as 'tonic', 'fuel' or 'food'. |
| **Calnan and Johnson (1985)** | To explore the relationship between occupational social class and dimensions of health beliefs about vulnerability to disease. | Qualitative: Semi-structured interviews. | Abstract concepts of health differed according to social class, though theories about vulnerability did not. |
| **Lupton (1995)** | To analyse front-page coverage of medical and health stories in *Sydney Morning Herald*. | Quantitative: Textual analysis. Qualitative: Discourse analysis. | Coverage of individualised illness rather than placing it in its broader socio-economic and political contexts. |
| **Lewis and Ross (1995)** | To investigate the social and historical context of the gay dance party phenomenon. | Qualitative: 16 semi-structured interviews with patrons and organisers in Sydney, Australia. | More ritualised social interaction, fulfilling social and psychological needs, developed in reaction to, e.g., threat of HIV. |

**Table 5 Control**

| Author(s) | Aims | Methods | Key points |
| --- | --- | --- | --- |
| **Umberson and Williams (1993)** | To consider possible reasons why parenting in the divorced status is conductive to parental role strain, distress and alcohol abuse. | Qualitative: In-depth interviews with 45 divorced fathers in the USA. | Patients take risks with physical health to exercise self-control over mental health, even when they know they are damaging their health, e.g. alcohol and drug abuse, physical violence. |
| **Bates and Rankin-Hill (1994)** | To assess the relationships between ethnic or cultural background and locus of control style in the chronic pain experience. | Quantitative: Questionnaire, examination of medical records, formal interviews with patients and clinicians. Qualitative: Formal and informal interviews; 6 patients selected from 7 ethno-cultural groups for intensive case-study interviews (recorded, transcribed and coded). In USA and Puerto Rico. | Locus of control (LoC) style not permanent and unchanging; in many ethnic and cultural groups increased sense of control contributes to increased ability to cope with chronic pain experience. Ethnicity and cultural group not absolute predictor of LoC style. It may be possible to alter a patient's sense of control through culturally appropriate and personally relevant programmes. |
| **Hack, Degner and Dyke (1994)** | To examine LoC style *re* relationships between cancer patients' preferences for information about treatment decisions: diagnosis, side effects, and prognosis. | Quantitative: Card sort measurement of preference. Qualitative: Semi-structured interviews with 35 English-speaking Canadian women with breast cancer, aged 32–38, to enable them to elaborate. | Patients who desired an active role in treatment decision-making also desired detailed information on diagnosis and treatment. Passive patients preferred that clinicians use euphemisms when referring to cancer. Cancer care should be tailored to the type of patient and their expressed preference for active or passive control of their illness. |
| **Scheid-Cook (1993)** | To examine out-patient commitment (OPC – legal mechanism of out-patient psychiatric treatment whereby patients report to clinic regularly for medication) from points of view of: clinicians (the controllers) and clients (the controlled). | Qualitative: In-depth interviews with 123 clinicians and 68 patients in North Carolina, USA over 2 years. Examination of medical records. | Clinicians see OPC as providing greater social control to professionals, whilst patients view OPC as providing greater self-control to patients relative to the ultimate confinement of the hospital. |
| **Waitzkin and Britt (1993)** | To see how patients and doctors communicate during medical encounters about the social context of self-destructive behaviours that warrant preventive action, such as smoking, substance use, and sexual practices. | Qualitative: Interpretive method in 50 encounters selected randomly from 336 audiotaped encounters involving patients and primary care internists, in the USA. | The discourse of health care reinforces ideological principles of professional surveillance and individual control in dealing with patients' self-destructive tendencies. Social context remains largely marginal to the discourse, despite its pertinence to the goal of prevention. |
| **Bowler (1993)** | To examine stereotypes of South Asian descent women held by midwives in a British hospital. | Qualitative: Small-scale ethnographic study interviewing 25 midwives and other personnel using open-ended questions, as well as general conversation during observation of midwife care. | Midwives stereotyped South Asian patients. This reflected and reinforced the view that Asian women are 'all the same' but 'not like us'. Midwives used stereotypes to help them make judgements about the kind of care different women wanted, needed and deserved. |
| **Matickatyndale (1992)** | To examine lay knowledge and its relation to scientifically based safer sex guidelines. | Qualitative: Semi-structured interviews with 25 Canadian college students. | An overriding rule of HIV protection was obtaining protection through the selection of uninfected partners. |

| Author(s) | Aims | Methods | Key points |
|---|---|---|---|
| **Ashworth and Hagan (1993)** | To explore how young and middle-aged women experience incontinence. | Qualitative: Semi-structured interviews. | The women felt stigmatised by their incontinence and perceived themselves as responsible for 'coping' with the condition |
| **Waitzkin (1989)** | To analyse control in medical encounters. | Qualitative: Observation of medical encounters; semi-structured interviews with patients and doctors. | Ideology and social control in medical discourse remain largely unintentional mechanisms of social control influenced by the technical structure of the medical encounter. |

**Table 6 Social support**

| Author(s) | Aims | Methods | Key points |
|---|---|---|---|
| **Lie and Biswalo (1994)** | To identify key characteristics of an HIV/AIDS counsellor who would prove to be culturally acceptable for the particular problems associated with HIV/AIDS in Tanzania. | Qualitative: Unstructured interviews and focus groups. | Despite differences in the cultural context, the data fit Western theories on client-centred counselling. Informants were more concerned with the social consequences of the disease than with the technical facts of AIDS, i.e. stigma and fear of rejection. |
| **Morgan and March (1992)** | To investigate the effects of different life events on networks of personal relationships through a comparison of recent widows and care-givers of a spouse with Alzheimer's disease. | Qualitative: Focus groups. Each negative, positive or neutral mention by widows or care-givers of members of their networks coded accordingly. | Widows had more people in their networks for whom they expressed feelings than care-givers Widowhood generates changes that have impacts throughout the social network, while care-giving leads to a life that is centred on the intense demands of caring for the spouse. Life events can affect relationships and social networks. |
| **Hildingh, Fridlund and Segesten (1995)** | To obtain in-depth information from members of a social support group for people with coronary heart disease (CHD) about lived experience of social support in a self-help group. | Qualitative: Unstructured interviews with 10 persons in a self-help group aged between 66 and 84, 6 of whom had CHD, 4 of whom were next of kin. | Group members' experience of social support indicate that the network is extremely important to the group members and enables them to cope, gain confidence and be optimistic. |
| **Kirk and Tinning (1994)** | To examine young people's body image. | Qualitative: Semi-structured interviews and focus groups with male and female adolescents. | Many adolescents experience 'disembodiment' in PE lessons to protect self-identity. Some fear revealing physical incompetence and so experience alienation. |

## Table 7 Prevention and lifestyle

| Author(s) | Aims | Methods | Key points |
|---|---|---|---|
| **Power et al. (1995)** | To illustrate the way coping strategies form an integral part of everyday lifestyles of injectors of illicit drugs. | Qualitative: Semi-structured survey with 100 respondents and 2 focus groups in England. | Social networks are characterised by functional and reciprocal relations. Peer education and health advocacy takes place on an informal basis. Rules and social etiquettes of networks not always positive for public health agenda. |
| **Sheilds (1995)** | To understand and develop the concept of empowerment from theoretical and practical perspectives, with a particular focus on women's perceptions of it in their lives. | Qualitative: In-depth semi-structured interviews with 15 women aged 21–71, who responded to a recruitment flyer and follow-up group participation. | Three central themes to women's perception of empowerment: development of an internal sense of self; ability to take action based on that; salient themes of connectedness. |
| **Siegel and Krauss (1991)** | To gain insights into the challenges of daily living faced by seropositive persons, to aid design of education on adaptive success. | Qualitative: Focused interviews with 55 seropositive gay men. | Three major adaptive challenges: curtailed life span; stigmatising illness; maintaining physical and emotional health. |
| **Backett and Davison (1995)** | To examine the cultural construction of physical and social ageing and lay views of its relevance to health behaviour. | Qualitative: In-depth interviews with 60 adults in Edinburgh, Scotland; unstructured interviews with, and observation of, 60 adults in South Wales; multi-interview of 28 middle-class couples in Edinburgh. | Respondents accounted for health and illness in terms of perceived social circumstances and obligations. Position in life course used to express these constellations of socio-cultural processes and variables. |
| **Mullen (1992)** | To focus on male Glaswegians' perceptions of the health effects of occupations. | Quantitative: 352 screening questionnaires on health, smoking and drinking. Qualitative: 70 unstructured interviews with men, aged 30–49, Glasgow, Scotland. | Respondents aware of influence of jobs on health; action taken either compensation or control of work environment. Commitment to work had bearing on coping style. |
| **Pill and Stott (1985b)** | To see the extent to which procedures (health service use) and practices (daily lifestyle choice) are interrelated and practised by the same people. | Qualitative: 204 women, aged 25–40, completed semi-structured interview schedule in South Wales. | No evidence to support proposition that preventive health behaviour is unidimensional, nor determined by independent dimensions. |
| **Punamaki and Kokko (1995)** | To examine reasons for consultation and explanations of illness. | Qualitative: Semi-structured interviews with patients consulting general practitioners in Finland. | Biomedical and lay constructs of illness overlap, as respondents' most common explanations for consultation related to infectious and toxic agents and constitutional physical defects rather than lifestyle or behavioural reasons. |
| **Rush et al. (1995)** | To explore family doctors' perceptions about interventions for alcohol use. | Qualitative: Semi-structured interviews and focus groups. | Strong support came from doctors for seeing alcohol use as a lifestyle issue and for a holistic approach to patient care. |
| **Prout (1989)** | To trace the relationships between sickness and the wider features of children's lives, especially at school. | Qualitative: Semi-structured interviews with children, mothers, teachers; health diaries; observation at school. | Sickness plays a central part in the construction of meaning around the transition from primary to secondary school. The concept of dominant symbol illuminates the data. |

| Author(s) | Aims | Methods | Key points |
|---|---|---|---|
| **Periard and Ames (1993)** | To assess perceptions of lifestyle changes and coping patterns of care-givers to stroke survivors. | Quantitative and qualitative methods and analysis with 20 care-givers. | Strains relative to care-giving may also be related to established patterns of daily life. |
| **Quatromoni *et al.*** | To assess cultural influences on diabetes prevention and management. | Qualitative: Focus group interviews with 30 urban Caribbean Latinos with diabetes mellitus and four family members. | Respondents described feelings of social isolation, fatalism, barriers to diet and exercise and lack of understanding of diabetes long term. |
| **d'Houtard and Field (1984)** | To determine definitions of health. | Qualitative: Open-ended questions asked of 4000 patients operationalised in France. | Higher classes defined health in personalised and positive terms; lower classes in negative and socialised terms. |

# References

Altheide, D and Johnson, J (1994). Criteria for assessing interpretive validity in qualitative research. In Denzin, N and Lincoln, Y (eds.) *Handbook of Qualitative Research*. Sage.

Anderson, J (1987). Migration and health: perspectives on immigrant women. *Sociology of Health and Illness* **9**:410.

Anderson, J M, Wiggins, S, Rajwani, R, Holbrook, A, Blue, C and Ng, M (1995). Living with a chronic illness – Chinese-Canadian and Euro-Canadian women with diabetes – exploring factors that influence management. *Social Science and Medicine* **41**(2):181–95.

Ashworth, P D, Hagan, M T, (1993). The meaning of incontinence – a qualitative study of non-geriatric urinary-incontinence sufferers. *Journal of Advanced Nursing* **18**(9):1415–23.

Backett, K C and Davison, C (1995). Lifecourse and lifestyle – the social and cultural location of health behaviours. *Social Science and Medicine* **40**(5):629–38.

Balshem, M, Oxman, G, Vanrooyen, D and Girod, K (1992). Syphilis, sex, and crack cocaine – images of risk and morality. *Social Science and Medicine* **35**(2):147–60.

Bates, M S and Rankin-Hill, L (1994). Control, culture and chronic pain. *Social Science and Medicine* **39**(5):629–45.

Beardall, S and Edwards, N (1995). The vegetarian option – varieties, conversions, motives and careers. *Sociological Review* **40**(2):253–93.

Bowes, A and Domokos, T M (1993). South Asian women and health services: a study in Glasgow. *New Community* **19**(4):611–26.

Blaxter, M (1990). *Health and Lifestyles*. Tavistock/Routledge.

Blaxter, M (1985). Self-definition of health status and consulting roles in primary care. *The Quarterly Journal of Social Affairs* **1**(2):134–74.

Blaxter, M and Paterson, E (1982). *Mothers and Daughters: a Three Generational Study of Health Attitudes and Behaviour*. Heinemann Education Books.

Bloor, M (1995). A user's guide to contrasting theories of HIV-related risk behaviour. In Gabe, J (ed.) *Medicine, Health and Risk*. Blackwell.

Bowler, I, (1993). 'They're not the same as us': midwives' stereotypes of South Asian descent maternity patients. *Sociology of Health and Illness* **15**(2):157.

Brown, P (1995). Popular epidemiology, toxic waste and social movements. In Gabe, J, (ed.). *Medicine, Health and Risk*. Blackwell.

Brown, P and Masterson-Allen, S (1994). Citizen action on toxic waste contamination: a new type of social movement. *Society and Natural Resources* **7**:269–86.

Browne, J and Minichiello, V (1994). The condom: why more people don't put it on. *Sociology of Health and Illness* **16**(20:229–52.

Brug, J, Debie, S, Vanassema, P and Weijts, W (1995). Psychosocial determinants of fruit and vegetable consumption among adults – results of focus group interviews. *Food, Quality and Preference* **6**(2):99–107

Calnan, M (1983). Managing 'minor' disorders. *Sociology of Health and Illness*. **5**:149.

Calnan, M (1988). Towards a conceptual framework of lay evaluation of health care. *Social Science and Medicine* **27**(9):927–33.

Calnan, M and Johnson, B (1985). Health, health risks and inequalities: an exploratory study of women's perceptions. *Sociology of Health and Illness* **7**:1.

Casey, J C, Griffin, M L and Googins, B K (1993). The role of work for wives of alcholics. *American Journal of Drug and Alcohol Abuse* **19**(1):119–31.

Chavez, L R, Hubbell, F A, McMullin, J M, Martinez, R G and Mishra, S I (1995). Structure and meaning in models of breast and cervical cancer risk factors – a comparison of perceptions among Latinas, Anglo women and physicians. *Medical Anthropology Quarterly* **9**(1):40–74.

Coggans, N and McKellar, S (1994). Drug use amongst peers – peer pressure or peer preference. *Drugs Education Prevention and Policy* **1**(1):15–26.

Coreil, J., Levin, J.S., Jaco, E.G., (1985), Lifestyle – an emergent concept in the sociomedical sciences, Culture Medicine Psychiatry, **9**, 423.

Cornwell J (1984). *Hard Earned Lives: Accounts of Health and Illness from East London* Tavistock.

DHSS (1980). *Inequalities in Health: Report of a Research Working Group* [Black Report]. DHSS.

Davison, C, Davey Smith, G and Frankel, S, (1991). Lay epidemiology and the prevention paradox: the implications of coronary candidacy for health education. *Sociology of Health and Illness* **13**(1)1–19.

De Swann, A (1990). *The Management of Normality*. London: Routledge.

Dean, K (ed.) (1994). *Population Health Research: Linking Theory and Methods*. Sage.

Denzin, N and Lincoln, Y (1994). *Handbook of Qualitative Research*. Sage

Department of Health (1995). *Variations in Health: What can the Department of Health and the NHS do?* Report produced by the Sub-group of the Chief Medical Officer's Health of the Nation Working Group.

Devine, C M and Olson, C M (1992). Women's perceptions about the way social roles promote or constrain personal nutrition care. *Women and Health* **19**(1):79–95.

Donovan, J, (1984). Ethnicity and health. *Social Science and Medicine* **19**(7):663–70.

Donovan, J (1986). *We Don't Buy Sickness, It Just Comes: Health, Illness and Health Care in the Lives of Black People in London*. Gower.

Douglas, M (1992). *Risk and Blame*. Routledge.

Eiser, J, Eiser, C, Gammage, P and Morgan, M (1989). Adolescent smoking – attitude, norms and parental influence. *British Journal of Addiction* 84(9):1059–65.

Giddens, A (1991). *Modernity and Self-identity*. Polity.

Goffman (1961). *Asylums*. Harmondsworth: Penguin.

Gottlieb, N H, Lovato, C Y, Weinstein, R, Green, L W and Eriksen, M P (1992). The implementation of a restrictive worksite smoking policy in a large decentralized organisation. *Health Education Quarterly* **19**(1):77–100.

Graham, H, (1987). Women's smoking and family health. *Social Science and Medicine* **25**(1):47–56.

Graham, H (1993). *Hardship and Health in Women's Lives*. Harvester Wheatsheaf.

Hack, T F, Degner, L F and Dyck, D G (1994). Relationship between preferences for decisional control and illness information among women with breast cancer – a quantitative and qualitative analysis. *Social Science and Medicine* **39**(2):279–89.

Hammersley, M (1992.) *What's Wrong with Ethnography?: Methodological Explorations*. London: Routledge.

Harris, D H and Guten, S (1979). Health-protective behaviour: an explanatory study. *Journal of Health and Social Behaviour* **20**:17–29.

Helman, C G (1981). 'Tonic, fuel and food.' Social and symbolic aspects of the long-term use of psychotropic drugs. *Social Science and Medicine* **15**b: 521–33.

Herzlich, C (1973). *Health and Illness, a Social Psychological Analysis*. London and New York: Academic Press.

Hildingh, C, Fridlund, B and Segesten, K (1995). Social support in self-help groups, as experienced by persons having coronary heart-disease and their next of kin. *International Journal of Nursing Studies* **32**(3):224–32.

Holland, J, Ramazonoglu, C, Sharpe, S and Thompson, R (1992). Pressured pleasure: young women and the negotiation of sexual boundaries. *Sociological Review* **40**:645–74.

Holm, L, (1993). Cultural and social acceptability of a healthy diet. *European Journal of Clinical Nutrition* 47(8):592–99.

d'Houtaud, A and Field, M, (1984). The image of health: variations in perception by social class in a French population. *Sociology of Health and Illness* **6**(1):30–60.

Kasl, S and Cobb, S (1966). Health behviour, illness behaviour and sick role behaviour. *Archives of Environmental Health* **12**:531–41.

Kirk *et al.* (1994). Embodied self-identity, healthy lifestyles and school physical education. *Sociology of Health and Illness* **16**(5):600.

Koniak-Griffin, D, Nyamathi, A, Vasquez, R and Russo, A A (1994). Risk-taking behaviors and AIDS knowledge – experiences and beliefs of minority adolescent mothers. *Health Education Research* **9**(4):449–63.

Lane, K (1995). The medical model of the body as a site of risk: a case study of childbirth. In Gabe, J (ed.) *Medicine, Health and Risk*. Blackwell.

Langlie, J K (1977). Social networks, health beliefs and preventive health behaviour. *Journal of Health and Social Behaviour* **18**:244–60.

Lawson, E J (1994). The role of smoking in the lives of low-income pregnant adolescents – a field study. *Adolescence* **29**(113): 61–79.

Lengua, L J, Roosa, M W, Schupakneuberg, E, Michaels, M L, Berg, C N and Weschler, L F (1992). Using focus groups to guide the development of a parenting program for difficult-to-reach, high-risk families. *Family Relations* **41**(2):163–8.

Lewis, L A and Ross, M W (1995). The gay dance party culture in Sydney – a qualitative analysis. *Journal of Homosexuality* **29**(1):41–70.

Lie, G T and Biswalo, P M (1994). Perceptions of the appropriate HIV/AIDS counsellor in Arusha and Kilimanjaro regions of Tanzania – implications for hospital counselling. *AIDS Care – Psychological and Socio-Medical Aspects of AIDS/HIV* **6**(2):139–51.

Lowy, E and Ross, M W, (1994). It'll never happen to me – gay men's beliefs, perceptions and folk constructions of sexual risk. *AIDS Education and Prevention* **6**(6):467–82.

Lupton, D (1995). Medical and health stories on the *Sydney Morning Herald*'s front page. *Australian Journal of Public Health* **19**(5):501.

Lupton, D and Chapman, S (1995). A healthy lifestyle might be the death of you – discourses on diet, cholesterol control and heart disease in the press and among the lay public. *Sociology of Health and Illness* **17**(4):477–94.

Matickatyndale, E, (1992). Social construction of HIV transmission and prevention among heterosexual young adults. *Social Problems* **39**(3):238–52.

Mayall, B (1993). Keeping health at home and school. *Sociology of Health and Illness* **15**(4):464.

McKeganey, N, Barnard, M and Bloor, M (1990). A comparison of HIV-related risk behaviour and risk reduction between female street working prostitutes and male rent boys in Glasgow. *Sociology of Health and Illness* **12**(3):274–92.

Merton, R K (1957). *Social Theory and Social Structure*. The Free Press.

Morgan, D L and March, S J (1992). The impact of life events on networks of personal relationships – a comparison of widowhood and caring for a spouse with Alzheimer's disease. *Journal of Social and Personal Relationships* **9**(4):563–84.

Morgan, G (ed.) (1983). *Beyond Method*. Beverley Hills.

Mullen, K (1992). A question of balance: health behaviour and work context among male Glaswegians. *Sociology of Health and Illness* **14**(1):73.

Mulrow, C (1994). Systematic reviews – rationale for systematic reviews. *British Medical Journal* **30**(9):597–9.

Pearson, M, Dawson, C, Moore, H and Spence, S (1993). Health on borrowed time? Prioritising and meeting needs in low income households. *Health and Social Care in the Community* **1**(1):45–55.

Periard, M E and Ames, B D (1993). Lifestyle changes and coping patterns among caregivers of stroke survivors. *Public Health Nursing* **10**(4):252–56.

Peterson, M and Johnstone, B M (1995). The Atwood-hall health promotion program, Federal Medical Centre, Lexington, Kentucky – effects of drug-involved federal offenders. *Journal of Substance Abuse Treatment* **12**(1):43–8.

Phillimore, P and Moffatt, S (1994). Discounted knowledge: local experience, environmental pollution and health. In Popay, J and Williams, G (eds.) *Researching the People's Health*. Routledge.

Pill, R and Stott, N C H (1982). Concepts of illness causation and responsibility: some preliminary data from a sample of working class mothers. *Social Science and Medicine* **16**:43–52.

Pill, R and Stott, N C H (1985). Choice or chance: further evidence on ideas of illness and responsibility for health. *Social Science and Medicine* **20**(10):981–91.

Pill, R and Stott, N C H (1985). Preventive procedures and practices among working class women: new data and fresh insights. *Social Science and Medicine* **21**:(9)975–83.

Plummer, K (1983). *Documents of Lie: An Introduction to the Problems and Literature of a Humanistic Method*. Allen and Unwin.

Popay, J, Bartley, M and Owen, C (1993). Gender inequalities in health: social position, affective disorders and minor physical morbidity. *Social Science and Medicine* **36**(1):21–32.

Popay, J, Williams, G and Bissell, P (1995). Public health risks in the material world: barriers to social movements in health. In Gabe, J (ed.) *Medicine, Health and Risks*. Blackwell.

Power, R, Jones, S, Kears, G, Ward, J and Perera, J (1995). Drug-user networks, coping strategies and HIV prevention in the community. *Journal of Drug Issues* **25**(3):565–81.

Prout (1989). Sickness as a dominant symbol in life course transitions: an illustrated theoretical framework. *Sociology of Health and Illness* **11**:336.

Punamaki, R-L and Kokko, S J (1995). Reasons for consultation and explanations of illness among Finnish primary care patients. *Sociology of Health and Illness* **17**(1):42.

Quatromoni, P A, Milbauer, M, Posner, B M, Carballeira, N P, Brunt, M and Chipkin, S R (1994). Use of focus groups to explore nutrition practices and health beliefs of urban Caribbean Latinos with diabetes. *Diabetes Care* **17**(8):869–73.

Rice, C, Roberts, H, Smith, S J and Bryce, C (1994). 'It's like teaching your child to swim in a pool full of alligators': lay voices and professional research on child accidents. In Popay, J and Williams, G. *Researching the People's Health*. Routledge.

Richards, M P M (1993). The new genetics: some issues for social scientists. *Sociology of Health and Illness* **15**(5):567–86.

Rigby, A and Hickey, D (1993). Women and children last? Class, health and the role of the maternal and child health services. *European Journal of Public Health* 220–6.

Ritchie, J E, Herscovitch, F and Norfor, J B (1994). Beliefs of blue-collar workers regarding coronary risk behaviors. *Health Education Research* **9**(1):95–103.

Roberts, H, Bryce, C and Smith, A (1993). Prevention is better. *Sociology of Health and Illness* **15**:447–59.

Rogers, A and Pilgrim, D (1995). The risk of resistance: perspectives on the mass childhood immunisation programme. In Gabe, J (ed.). *Medicine, Health and Risk*. Sociology of Health and Illness Monograph. Blackwell.

Rogers, A, Pilgrim, D and Latham, M (1996). *Understanding and Promoting Mental Health: a Study of Familial Views and Conduct in their Social Contexts*. Health Education Authority.

Rush, B R, Powell, L Y, Crowe, T G and Ellis, K (1995). Early interventions for alcohol use – family physicians' motivations and perceived barriers. *Canadian Medical Association Journal* **152**(6):863–9.

Scheid–Cook, T L (1993), Controllers and controlled – an analysis of participant constructions of outpatient commitment. *Sociology of Health and Illness* **15**(2):179–98.

Sharma, U (1992). *Complementary Medicine Today: Practitioners and Patients*. London: Tavistock/Routledge.

Sheilds, L E (1995). Women's experiences of the meaning of empowerment. *Qualitative Health Research* **5**(1):15–35.

Siegel, K and Krauss, B J (1991). Living with HIV infection: adaptive tasks of seropositive gay men. *Journal of Health and Social Behavior*. **32**:17–32.

Silverman (1987). *Qualitative Methodology and Sociology*. Gower.

Skolbekken, J A (1995). The risk of epidemic in medical journals. *Social Science and Medicine* **40**(3):291–305.

Sparks, G, Craven, M A and Worth, C (1994). Understanding differences between high and low childhood accident rate areas – the importance of qualitative data. *Journal of Public Health Medicine* **16**(4):439–46.

Stanley, L (1990) Doing ethnography, writing ethnography: a comment on Hammersley. *Sociology* **24**(4):617–27.

Stone, D (1989). Casual stories and the formation of policy agendas. *Political Science Quarterly* **104**(2):281–300.

Thomas, C (1995). Domestic labour and health: bringing it all back home. *Sociology of Health and Illness* **17**(3):328.

Tuchman, G and Levine, H G (1993). New York Jews and Chinese food – the social construction of an ethnic pattern. *Journal of Contemporary Ethnography* **22**(3):382–407.

Umberson, D and Williams, C L (1993). Divorced fathers – parental role strain and psychological distress. *Journal of Family Issues* **14**(3):378–400.

Waddell, A and Floate, D (1986). Gender and the utilisation of health care services in Perth, Australia: Research note. *Sociology of Health and Illness* **8**:170.

Waitzkin, H and Britt, T (1993). Processing narratives of self-destructive behavior in routine medical encounters – health promotion, disease prevention, and the discourse of health-care. *Social Science and Medicine* **36**(9):1121–36.

Waitzkin, H, Britt, T and Williams, C (1994). Narratives of aging and social problems in medical encounters with older persons. *Journal of Health and Social Behaviour* **35**:322–48.

Wearing, B, Wearing, S and Kelly, K (1994). Adolescent women, identity and smoking: leisure experience as resistance. *Sociology of Health and Illness* **16**(5)626.

Whitehead, M (1987). *The Health Divide*. Health Education Council.

WHO Health Education Unit (1986). Lifestyles and health. *Social Science and Medicine* **22**:117.

Wight, D (1993). *Workers not Wasters*. Edinburgh University Press.

Williams, G and Popay, J (1994). Lay knowledge and the privilege of experience. In Gabe, J, Kelleher, D and Williams, G, (eds.). *Challenging Medicine*. Routledge.

Williams, G, Popay, J and Bissell, P (1995). Public health risks in the material world: barriers to social movements in health. In Gabe, J (ed.). *Medicine, Health and Risks*. Blackwell.

Williams, G H and Wood, P H N (1986). Patients and their illnesses: common-sense beliefs about illnesses: a mediating role for the doctor. *Lancet* 20/27 December p. 1435.

Williams, S J and Calnan, M (1994). Perspectives on prevention: the views of general practitioners. *Sociology of Health and Illness* **16**(3):372–93.

Wing, S (1994). Limits of epidemiology. *Medicine and Global Survival* **1**:74–86.

Wood, R C (1995). *The Sociology of the Meal*. Edinburgh University Press.

Woolfe, S, Battista, R and Anderson, G (1993). Assessing the clinical effectiveness of preventive manoeuvres: analytic principles and systematic methods in reviewing evidence and developing clinical practice recommendations. *Journal of Clinical Epidemiology* **43**: 891–905

Woollett, A, Dosanjh, N, Nicolson, P, Marshall, H and Djhanbakch, O (1995). The ideas and experiences of pregnancy and childbirth of Asian and non-Asian women in East London. *British Journal of Medical Psychology* **68**(1):65–84.

Wright, P (1987). The social construction of babyhood: the definition of infant care as a medical problem. In Bryman, A, Bytheway, B, Allatt, P and Keil, T. *Rethinking the Lifecycle*. Macmillan.

Zola, I K (1973). Pathways to the doctor – from person to patient. *Social Science and Medicine* **7**:677–89.

# Bibliography

Ahmed, A F, Osman, A K, Bustami, A B, Aldirwish, S and Bashir, S (1993). A pilot study of diet and gallstone formation in young Saudi women. *Journal of the Royal Society of Health* **113**(2):57–9.

Ambert, A-M (1982). Drug use in separated/divorced persons. *Social Science and Medicine* **16**:971–76.

Anderson, J (1986). Ethnicity and illness experience: ideological structures and the health care delivery system. *Social Science and Medicine* **22**(11):1277–83.

Anderson, J, Elfert, H and Lai, M (1989). Ideology in the clinical context: Chronic illness, ethnicity and the discourse on normalisation. *Sociology of Health and Illness* **11**:3.

Arnow, B, Kenardy, J and Agras, W S (1992). Binge eating among the obese – a descriptive study. *Journal of Behavioural Medicine* **15**(2):155–70.

Backett, K (1987). *The Achievement of Health – the Middle Classes Discuss Health in Families.* (Working Paper No. 13), Edinburgh: Research Unit in Health and Behavioural Change.

Backett, K (1988). *Studying Health in Families: a Qualitative Approach.* Edinburgh: Research Unit in Behavioural Change.

Backett, K (1992). Taboos and excesses: lay health moralities in middle class families. *Sociology of Health and Illness* **14**(2):255–74.

Banks C G (1992). Culture in culture-bound syndromes – the case of anorexia nervosa. *Social Science and Medicine* **34**(8)867–84.

Bauman, L J and Adair, E G (1992). The use of ethnographic interviewing to inform questionnaire construction. *Health Education Quarterly* **19**(1):9–23.

Beardall, S and Edwards, N (1995). Social and cultural determinants of smoking behaviour in selected immigrant groups – results of key informant interviews. *Family and Community Health* **18**(2):65–72.

Beardsworth, A and Keil, T (1992). The varietism option – varietism conversions, motives and careers. *Sociological Review* **40**(2):253–93.

Bendelow, G (1993). Pain perceptions, emotions and genders. *Sociology of Health and Illness* **15**:3.

Black, M E A (1995). What did women's magazines from 1929 to 1949 say about breast-cancer? *Cancer Nursing* **18**(4):270–77.

Black, M M and Ricardo, I B (1994). Drug use, drug trafficking, and weapon carrying among low-income African-American early adolescent boys. *Pediatrics* **93**(6):1065–72.

Blane, D, Davey Smith, D and Bartley, M (1993). Social selection: what does it contribute to social class differences in health? *Sociology of Health and Illness* **15**:1.

Blanz, B J, Renschriemann, B S, Fritzigmund, D I and Schmidt, M H (1993). IDDM is a risk factor for adolescent psychiatric disorders. *Diabetes Care* **16**(12);1579–87.

Blaxter, M (1985). Why do the victims blame themselves? In Radley, A (ed.). *Worlds of Illness: Biographical and Cultural Perspectives on Health and Disease.* Routledge.

Blaxter, M and Cyster, R (1984). Compliance and risk-taking: the case of alcoholic liver disease. *Sociology of Health and Illness* **6**(3):419–31.

Bowling, A (1994). Beliefs about illness causation among Turkish and white British people living in a deprived inner London district. *Health Education Research* **9**(3):355–64.

Bradby, H (1995). Of heating and heart attacks: understanding of health and food among young British Asian women. Paper presented at BSA Medical Sociology Group conference, York. 22–24 September.

Brendstrup, E and Schmidt, K (1990). Homosexual and bisexual men's coping with the AIDS epidemic: qualitative interviews with 10 non-HIV tested homosexual and bisexual men. *Social Science and Medicine* **30**(6):713–20.

Burr, A (1984). The ideologies of despair: a symbolic interpreation of punks' and skinheads' usage of barbiturates. *Social Science and Medicine* **19**(9):929–38.

Bury, M, Gabe, J (1990). Hooked? The media's response to tranquilliser dependence. In Abbott, O and Payne, G (eds.) *New Directions in the Sociology of Health*. Falmer.

Caballodieguez, A and Dolezal, C (1995). Association between history of childhood sexual abuse and adult HIV risk sexual behaviour in Puerto-Rican men who have sex with men. *Child Abuse and Neglect* **19**(5):595–605.

Calnan, M and Williams, S (1991). Style of life and salience of health. *Sociology of Health and Illness* **13**:506.

Carricabaru, D and Pierret, J (1995). From biographical disruption to biographical reinforcement: the case of HIV-positive men. *Sociology of Health and Illness* **17**(1):65–88.

Carrigan, J T (1994). The psychosocial needs of patients who have attempted suicide by overdose. *Journal of Advanced Nursing* **20**(4):635–42.

Chapman, S (1993). Unravelling gossamer with boxing gloves – problems in explaining the decline in smoking. *British Medical Journal* **307**(6901):429–32.

Chesham, D J, Rutter, D R and Quine, L (1993). Motorcyling safety research – a review of the social behavioural literature. *Social Science and Medicine* **347**(3):419–29.

Clarke, R and Lowe, F (1989). Positive health – some lay perspectives. *Health Promotion* **3**(4):401–6.

Conrad, P (1979). Types of medical social control. *Sociology of Health and Illness* **1**(1):1–20.

Conrad, P (1988). Health and fitness at work: a participant's perspective. *Social Science and Medicine* **26**(5):545–50.

Cooperstock, R and Lennard, H L (1979). Some social meanings of tranquilizer use. *Sociology of Health and Illness* **1**(3):324–38.

Coreil, J, Levin, J S and Jaco, E G (1985). Lifestyle – an emergent concept in the sociomedical sciences. *Culture, Medicine and Psychiatry* **9**:423.

Coxon, T (1988). Social science and AIDS (Review essay). *Sociology of Health and Illness* **10**:608.

Creswell, C M, Kuipers, L and Power, M. J (1992). Social networks and support in long-term psychiatric patients. *Psychological Medicine* **22**(4):1019–26.

Crotty, P A, Rutishauser, I H E and Cahill, M (1992). Food in low-income families. *Australian Journal of Public Health* **16**(2):168–74.

DHSS (1980). *Inequalities in Health: Report of a Working Group* [Black Report]. DHSS.

Davies, C (1984). General practioners and the pull of prevention. *Sociology of Health and Illness* **6**:267.

Davison, C, Frankel S and Smith G D (1992). The limits of lifestyle: reassessing 'fatalism' in the popular culture of illness prevention. *Social Science and Medicine* **34**:675.

Deering, M J (1993). Designing health promotion approaches to high-risk adolescents through formative research with youth and parents. *Public Health Reports* **108**(1):68–77

Devries, H, Weijts, W, Dijkstra, M and Kok, G (1992). The utilization of qualitative and quantitative data for health education program planning, implementation, and evaluation – a spiral approach. *Health Education Quarterly* **19**(1):101–15.

Dezwaan, M and Mitchell, J E (1994). Eating related and general psychopathology in obese females with binge-eating disorder. *International Journal of Eating Disorders* **15**(1):43–52.

Dickinson, R and Bhatt, A (1994). Ethnicity, health and control: results from an exploratory study of ethnic minority communities' attitudes to health. *Health Education Journal* **53**:421–29.

Dorfman, L E, Derish, P A and Cohen, J B (1992). Hey girlfriend – an evaluation of AIDS prevention among women in the sex industry. *Health Education Quarterly* **19**(1):25–40.

Dressler, W W (1985). The social and cultural context of coping: action, gender and symptions in a Southern black community. *Social Science and Medicine* **21**(5):499–506.

Elkind, A K, Haran, D, Eardley, A and Spencer, B (1988). Reasons for non-attendance for computer-managed cervical screening: pilot interviews. *Social Science and Medicine* **27**(6):651–60.

Elliott, H (1995). Community nutrition education for people with coronary heart-disease – who attends. *Australian Journal of Public Health* **19**(2):205–10.

Eng, E, (1993). The Save our Sisters projects – a social network strategy for reaching rural black women. *Cancer* **72**(3):1071–7.

Erdman, R A M , Horstman, L , Vandomburg, R T , Meeter, K and Balk, A H H M (1993). Compliance with the medical regimen and partners' quality of life after heart transplantation. *Quality of Life Research* **2**(3):205–12.

Fisher, S, (1984). Doctor-patient communication: a social and micro-political performance. *Sociology of Health and Illness* **6**(1):28–40.

Fitzpatrick, R *et al.* (1984). *The Experience of Illness*. See especially Scambler, G. Perceiving and coping with stigmatizing illness; Thompson, J. Compliance; Newman, S. Anxiety, hospitalization, and surgery. Tavistock.

Ford, N J and Kittisuksathit, S (1994). Destinations unknown – the gender construction and changing nature of the sexual expressions of Thai youth. *AIDS Care – Psychological and Socio-Medical Aspects of AIDS/HIV* **6**(5):517–31.

Forrest, K A, Austin, D M, Valdes, M I, Fuentes, E G and Wilson, S R (1993). Exploring norms and beliefs related to AIDS-prevention among Californian Hispanic men. *Family Planning Perspectives* **25**(3):111–17.

French, D J, Nicki, R M and Cane, D B (1993). Bulimia nervosa – an examination of the anxiety-inhibiting properties of the prospect of vomiting. *Behavioural Psychotherapy* **21**(2):97–106.

Freudenberg, N, Lee, J and Germain, L M (1994). Reaching low-income women at risk of AIDS – a case history of a drop-in centre for women in the South Bronx, New York City. *Health Education Research* **9**(1):105–18.

Gabe, J, Gustafsson, U and Bury, M (1991). Mediating illness: newspaper coverage of tranquilliser dependence. *Sociology of Health and Illness* **13**(3):332.

Gala, C, Pergami, A, Catalan, J, Durbano, F, Musicco A, Riccio, M, Baldeweg, T and Invernizzi, G (1993). The psychosocial impact of HIV infection in gay men, drug users and heterosexuals – controlled investigation. *British Journal of Psychiatry* **163**:651–9.

Gerhardt, U (1979). Coping and social action: theoretical reconstruction of the life-event approach. *Sociology of Health and Illness* **10**:195.

Glanz, K, Brekke, M, Harper, D, Backewig, M and Hunninghake, D B (1992). Evaluation of implementation of a cholesterol management program in physicians' offices. *Health Education Research* **7**(2):151–63.

Glik, D C, Greaves, P E, Kronenfeld, J J and Jackson, K L (1993). Safety hazards in households with young children. *Journal of Pediatric Psychology* **18**(1):115–31.

Glik, D C, Ward, W B, Gordon, A and Haba, F (1989). Malaria treatment practices among mothers in Guinea. *Journal of Health and Social Behaviour* **30**:421–35.

Goddman, E (1984). *Stigma: Notes on the Management of Spoiled Identity.* Penguin Books.

Goodman, E and Berecochea, J E (1994). Predictors of HIV testing among runaway and homeless adolescents. *Journal of Adolescent Health* **15**(7):566–72.

Gottlieb, N H, Lovato, C Y, Weinstein, R, Green, L W and Eriksen, M P (1992). The implementation of a restrictive worksite smoking policy in a large decentralized organisation. *Health Education Quarterly* **19**(1)77–100.

Gray, D E (1993). Perceptions of stigma: the parents of autistic children. *Sociology of Health and Illness* **15**(1):102.

Guest, C S and Odea, K (1993). Food habits in Aborigines and persons of European descent in Southeastern Australia. *Australian Journal of Public Health* **17**(4):321–4.

Guthrie, S R, Ferguson, C and Grimmett, D (1994). Elite women bodybuilders – ironing out nutritional misconceptions. *Sport Psychologist* **8**(3):271–89.

Harrison, G G, Zaghloul, S S, Galal, O M and Gabr, A (1993). Breast feeding and weaning in a poor urban neighbourhood in Cairo, Egypt – maternal beliefs and perceptions. *Social Science and Medicine* **36**(8):1063–9.

Harrison, M J, Neufeld, A and Kushner, K (1995). Women in transition – access and barriers to social support. *Journal of Advanced Nursing* **21**(5):858–64.

Hart *et al.* (1992). 'Relapse' to unsafe sexual behaviour amongst gay men: a critique of recent behavioural HIV/AIDS research. *Sociology of Health and Illness* **14**:216.

Hastings, G B, Ryan, H, Teer, P and Mackintosh, A M (1994). Cigarette advertising and children's smoking – why Reg was withdrawn. *British Medical Journal* **309**(6959):933–7.

Helman, C G (1981). 'Tonic', 'fuel', and 'food': social and symbolic aspects of the long-term use of psychotropic drugs. *Social Science and Medicine,* **15B**:521–33.

Henderson, K A and Bedini, L A (1995). I have a soul that dances like Tina Turner, but my body can't – physical activity and women with mobility impairments. *Research Quarterly for Exercise and Sport* **66**(2):151–61.

Henriksson, C M, (1995). Living with continuous muscular pain – patient perspectives on strategies of daily life. *Scandinavian Journal of Caring Sciences* **9**(2):77–86.

Hepworth, J (1994). Qualitative analysis and eating disorders – discourse analysis research on anorexia-nervosa. *International Journal of Eating Disorders* **15**(2):179–85.

Herzlich, C (1973). *Health and Illness: a Social-Psychological Analysis.* Academic Press.

Holderness C C, Brooksgunn, J and Warren, J P (1994). Eating disorders and substance use – a dancing vs. nondancing population. *Medicine and Science in Sports and Exercise* **26**(3):297–302.

Irwin, K, Bertrand, J, Mibandaumba, N, Mbuyi, K, Muremeri, C, Mukoka, M, Munkolenkole, K, Nzilambi, N, Bosenge, N, Ryder, R, Peterson, H, Lee, N C, Wingo, P, O'Reilly, K and Rufo, K (1991). Knowledge, attitudes and beliefs about HIV infection and AIDS among healthy factory workers and their wives. Kinshasa, Zaire. *Social Science and Medicine* **32**(3):917.

Ives, D G, Bonino, P, Traven, N D and Kuller, L H (1993). Morbidity and mortality in rural community-dwelling elderly with low total serum-cholesterol. *Journals of Gerontology* **48**(3):M103–M107.

Johnston, D, Stall, R and Smith, K (1995). Reliance by gay men and intravenous-drug-users on friends and family for AIDS-related care. *AIDS Care – Psychological and Socio-Medical Aspects of AIDS/HIV* **7**(3):307–19.

Johnson, J and Williams, M L (1993). A preliminary ethnographic decision tree model of injection drug users (IDUs) needle sharing. *International Journal of the Addictions* **28**(10):997–1014.

Joseph, D H and Patterson, B (1994). Risk-taking and its influence on metabolic control – a study of adult clients with diabetes. *Journal of Advanced Nursing* **19**(1):77–84.

Karpf, A (1988). *Doctoring the Media: the Reporting of Health and Medicine.* Routledge.

Kaufert, P A (1982). Myth and the menopause. *Sociology of Health and Illness.* **4**(2):141–66.

Keene, J M and Cervetto, S (1995). Health promotion in community pharmacy: a qualitative study. *Health Education Journal* **54**:285–93.

Keith, P M, Schafer, R B and Schafer, E (1995). Wives' relationships with food and patterns of family distress. *Social Behaviour and Personality* **23**(2)111–22.

Kitzinger, J (1994). The methodology of focus groups: the importance of interaction between research participants. *Sociology and Health and Illness* **16**(1):103.

Kleinman, K (1979). Emergency room use and access to alternative sources of care. *Sociology of Health and Illness* **1**(2):318–36.

Kotarba, J A and Bentley, P (1988). Workplace wellness participation and the becoming of self. *Social Science and Medicine* **26**(5):551–8.

Lacey, L P, Manfredi, C, Balch, G, Warneche, R B, Allen, K and Edwards, C (1993). Social support in smoking cessation among black women in Chicago public housing. *Public Health Reports* **108**(3)387–94.

Lagreca, A M, Auslander, W F, Greco, P, Spetter, D, Fisher, E B and Santiago, J V (1995). I get by with a little help from my family and friends – adolescents support for diabetes care. *Journal of Pediatric Psychology* **20**(4):449–76.

Lantz, P M, Dupuis, L, Reding, D, Krauska, M and Lappe, K (1994). Peer discussions of cancer among hispanic migrant farmworkers. *Public Health Reports* **109**(4):512–20.

Lasch, C (1979). *Culture of Narcissism.* New York: Norton.

Lee, S (1995). Self-starvation in context – towards a culturally sensitive understanding of anorexia nervosa. *Social Science and Medicine* **41**(1):25–36.

Lewis, L A and Ross, M W (1995). The gay dance party culture in Sydney – a qualitative analysis. *Journal of Homosexuality* **29**(1):41–70.

Lewis, V J, Blair, A J and Booth, D A (1992). Outcome of group therapy for body image emotionally and weight control self-efficacy. *Behavioural Psychotherapy* **20**(2):155–65.

Lieban, R W (1992). From illlness to symbol and symbol to illness. *Social Science and Medicine* **35**(2):183–8.

Long, A and Mullen, B (1994). An exploration of women's perceptions of the major factors that contributed to their alcohol-abuse. *Journal of Advanced Nursing* **19**(4):623–39.

Lupton, D (1995). Medical and health stories on the *Sydney Morning Herald*'s front page. *Australian Journal of Public Health* **19**(5):501.

Lupton, D, McCarthy, S and Chapman, S (1995). 'Panic bodies': discourse on risk and HIV antibody testing. *Sociology of Health and Illness* **17**(1):89–108.

Macintyre, S (1994). Understanding the social patterning of health: the role of the social sciences. *Journal of Public Health Medicine* **16**(1):53–9.

Magi, M and Allander, E (1981). Towards a theory of perceived and medically defined need. *Sociology of Health and Illness* **3**(1):49–71.

Markova, I, Wilkie, P A, Naji, S A and Forbes C D (1990). Self and other-awareness of the risk of HIV/AIDS in people with haemophilia and implications for behavioural change. *Social Science and Medicine* **31**(1):49–71.

Matickatyndale, E, Kiewying, M, Haswellelkins, M, Kuyyakanond, T, Anursornteerakul, S, Shantapreeda, N, Choosathan, R, Sornchai, S, Theerasobhon, P, Supornpun, A, Siriwattanametanont, J and Elkins, A (1994). Knowledge, attitudes and beliefs about HIV AIDS among women in North Eastern Thailand. *AIDS Education and Prevention* **6**(3):205–18.

Matickatyndale, E (1992). Social construction of HIV transmission and prevention among heterosexual young adults. *Social Problems* **39**(3):238–52.

Mayo, K (1992). Physical activity practices among American black working women. *Qualitative Health Research.* **2**(3):318–33.

McCourt, J and Waller, G (1995). Developmental role of perceived parental control in the eating psychopathology of Asian and Caucasian schoolgirls. *International Journal of Eating Disorders* **17**(3):277–82.

McKenna, J W and Williams, K N (1993). Crafting effective tobacco counteradvertisements – lessons from a failed campaign directed at teenagers. *Public Health Reports* **108**(S1):85–9.

McKie, L *et al.* (1993). Defining and assessing risky behaviours. *Journal of Advanced Nursing* **18**:1911–16.

McKie, L (1995). The art of surveillance or reasonable prevention? The case of cervical screening. *Sociology of Health and Illness* **17**(4):441–57.

Milburn, K and McAskill, S (1994). Cervical screening: continuing concerns in the 1990s. *Health Education Journal* **53**:201–13.

Morgan, Watkins (1988). Managing hypertension: beliefs and responses to medication among cultural groups. *Sociology of Health and Illness* **10**:561.

Morrell, S, Taylor, R, Quine, S and Kerr, C (1993). Suicide and unemployment in Australia, 1907–1990. *Social Science and Medicine* **36**(6):749–56.

Mulvaney, J (1994). Medicalisation, marginalization and control. In Waddell, C and Petersen, A R. *Just Health: Inequality in Illness, Care and Prevention*.

Murcott, A (1980). The social construction of teenage pregnancy: a problem in the ideologies of childhood and reproduction. *Sociology of Health and Illness* **2**(1):1.

Nelson, G, Wiltshire, C, Hall, G B, Peirson, L and Walshbowers, R (1995). Psychiatric consumer survivors quality-of-life-quantative and qualitative perspectives. *Journal of Community Psychology* **23**(3):216–33.

Nijhof, G (1995). Parkinson's disease as a problem of stigma in public appearance. *Sociology of Health and Illness* **17**(2):193–205.

Nourjah, P, Wagener, D K, Eberhardt, M and Horowitz, A M (1994). Knowledge of risk factors and risk behaviors related to coronary heart disease among blue and white collar males. *Journal of Public Health Policy* **15**(4):443–59.

O'Doherty, F (1991). Is drug use a response to stress? *Drug and Alcohol Dependence* **29**(1):97–106.

O'Donnell, L, Sandoval, A, Vornfett, R and Dejong, W (1994). Reducing AIDS and other STDs among inner-city Hispanics – the use of qualitative research in the development of video-based education. *AIDS Education and Prevention* **6**(20):140–53.

Oakley, A (1992). *Social Support and Motherhood: the Natural History of a Research Project*. Oxford University Press.

Ostergreen, P O, Hanson, B S, Isacsson, S O and Tejler, L (1991). Social network, social support and acute chest complaints among young and middle-aged patients in an emergency department – a case-control study. *Social Science and Medicine* **33**(3):257–67.

Ostergreen, P O, Lindbladh, E, Isacsson, S O, Odeberg H and Svensson, S E (1995). Social network, social support and the concept of control – a qualitative study concerning the validity of certain stressor measures used in quantitative social epidemiology. *Scandinavian Journal of Social Medicine* **23**(2)95–102.

Parsons, E and Atkinson, P (1992). Lay construction of genetic risk. *Sociology of Health and Illness* **14**(4).

Perezstable, E J, Sabogal, F, Oterosabogal, R, Hiatt, R A and McPhee, S J (1992). Misconceptions about cancer among Latinos and Anglos. *JAMA: Journal of the American Medical Association* **268**(22):3219–23.

Popay, J, Rogers, A and Williams, G (1996). Qualitative Research and the Gingerbreadman. *Health Education Journal* (editorial) **55**(1):1–3.

Pope, H G, Mangweth, B, Negrao, A B, Hudson, J I and Cordas, T A (1994). Childhood sexual abuse and bulimia nervosa – a comparison of American, Austrian and Brazilian women. *American Journal of Psychiatry* **151**:732–7.

Pound, P, Bury, M, Gompertz, P and Ebrahim, S (1995). Stroke patients' views on their admission to hospital. *British Medical Journal* **311**:18–22.

Pratt, C, Hill, S, Elliott, E and Popay, J (1994). *Social Support and the Health and Welfare of Young Children Stage 2: A Multicultural Perspective* (PHRRC Unpublished Project Report).

Prout (1986). 'Wet children' and 'little actresses': going sick in primary school. *Sociology of Health and Illness* **8**:111.

Quandt, S A, Popyach, J B and Dewalt, K M (1994). Home gardening and food preservation practices of the elderly in rural Kentucky. *Ecology of Food and Nutrition* **31**(3–4):183–99.

Ravallion, M (1992). Does undernutrition respond to incomes and prices? – dominance tests for Indonesia. *World Bank Economic Review* **6**(1):109–24

Reid, G J, Dubow, E F, Carey, T C and Dura, J R (1994). Contribution of coping to medical adjustment and treatment responsibility among children and adolescents with diabetes. *Journal of Developmental and Behavioural Pediatrics* **15**(5):327–35.

Rhodes, T and Stimson, G V (1994). What is the relationship between drug taking and sexual risk? Social relations and social research. *Sociology of Health and Illness* **16**(2):209–20.

Richardson, S and Pearson, M (1995). Dignity and aspiration denied: unmet health and social care needs in an inner-city area. *Health and Social Care in the Community* **3**(5):279–342.

Richter, L M and Swartkruger, J (1995), AIDS risk among street children and youth – implications for intervention. *South African Journal of Psychology* **25**(1):31–8.

Robinson, R B, Frank, D I (1994). The relation between self-esteem, sexual activity and pregnancy. *Adolescence* **29**(113):27–35.

Rogers, A and Pilgrim, D (1997). The contribution of lay knowledge to understanding and promoting mental health. *Journal of Mental Health* **6**(1):21–34.

Ropers, R H and Boyer, R (1987). Perceived health status among the new urban homeless. *Social Science and Medicine* **24**(8):669–78.

Rorty, M, Yager, J and Rossotto, E (1993). Why and how do women recover from bulimia nervosa – the subjective appraisals of 40 women recovered for a year or more. *International Journal of Eating Disorders* **14**(3):249–60.

Rosenthal, D A and Shepherd, H (1993). A 6-month follow-up of adolescents sexual risk-taking, HIV/AIDS knowledge and attitudes to condoms. *Journal of Community and Applied Social Psychology* **3**(1):53–65.

Russell, J (1982). Perinatal mortality: the current debate. *Sociology of Health and Illness* **4**(3):302–19.

Salazar, M K (1994). Breast self-examination beliefs – a descriptive study. *Public Health Nursing* **11**(1): 49–56.

Salazar, W A and Demoor, C (1995). An evaluation of mammography beliefs using a decision-model. *Health Education Quarterly* **22**(1):110–26.

Scambler, G and Hopkins, A (1990). Generating a model of epileptic stigma: the role of qualitative analysis. *Social Science and Medicine* **30**(11):1187–94.

Schneider, J W and Conrad, P (1981). Medical and sociological typologies: the case of epilepsy. *Social Science and Medicine* **15A**:211–19.

Schoenbach, V J, Orleans, C T, Wagner, E H, Quade, D, Salmon, M A P and Porter, C Q (1992). Characteristics of smokers who enroll and quit in self-help programs. *Health Education Research* **7**(30):369–80.

Sharma, S (1992). Supping and Sipping: an Exploration of the Role of Alcohol in the Lives of People in North Manchester. North Manchester Health Promotion.

Silverman, D (1985). *Qualitative Methodology and Sociology.* Gower.

Simpson, W S and Ramberg, J A (1992). Sexual dysfunction in married female patients with anorexia and bulimia nervosa. *Journal of Sex and Marital Therapy* **18**(1):44–54.

Singer, N (1995). Understanding sexual risk behaviour from drug-users accounts of their life experiences. *Qualitative Health Research* **5**(2):237–49.

Singleton, J C, Achterberg, C L and Shannon, B M (1992). Role of food and nutrition in the health perceptions of young children. *Journal of the American Dietetic Association* **92**(1):67–70.

Snadden, D and Brown, J B (1992). The experience of asthma. *Social Science and Medicine* **34**(12):1351–61.

Stevens, N (1995). Gender and adaptation to widowhood in later life. *Ageing and Society* **15**(1):37–58.

Stevens, P E (1994). HIV prevention education for lesbians and bisexual women – a cultural analysis of a community intervention. *Social Science and Medicine* **39**(11):1565–78.

Strong, P M (1980). Doctors and dirty work – the case of alcoholism. *Sociology of Health and Illness* **2**(1):150–61.

Sun, W Y and Chen, W W (1994). A preliminary study of potential dietary risk factors for coronary heart disease among Chinese–American adolescents. *Journal of School Health* **64**(9):368–71.

Sundgotborgen, J (1994). Risk and trigger factors for the development of eating disorders in female elite athletes. *Medicine and Science in Sports and Exercise* **26**(4):414–19.

Tang, L H, Manderson, L, Deng, D, Wu, K C, Cai, X Z, Lan, C X, Gu, Z C and Wang, K A (1995). Social aspects of malaria in Heping, Hainan. *Acta Tropica* **59**(1):41–53.

Thoits, P A (1995). Stress, coping and social processes – where are we? What next? *Journal of Health and Social Behaviour*. Extra Issue 53–79.

Thompson, K E and Range, L M (1993). Bereavement following suicide and other deaths – why support attempts fail. *Omega – Journal of Death and Dying* **26**(1):61–70.

Vize, C M and Cooper, P J (1995). Sexual abuse in patients with eating disorder, patients with depression and normal controls – a comparative study. *British Journal of Psychiatry* **167**:80–5.

Wagner, K G and Calhoun, L G (1992). Perceptions of social support by suicide survivors and their social networks. *Omega – Journal of Death and Dying* **24**(1):61–73.

Waitzkin, H (1989). A critical theory of medical discourse: ideology, social control, and the processing of social context in medical encounters. *Journal of Health and Social Behavior* **30**:220–39.

Waldby, D (1993). Heterosexual men and 'safe sex' practice (research note). *Sociology of Health and Illness* **15**:246.

Wallerstein, N and Sanchezmerki, V (1994). Freiran-praxis in health education – research results from an adolescent prevention program. *Health Education Research* **9**(1):105–18.

Warwick, I, Aggleton, P and Homans, H (1988). Constructing commonsense – young people's beliefs about AIDS. *Sociology of Health and Illness* **10**(3):274–89.

Watts, R J (1993). Community action through manhood development – a look at concepts and concerns from the frontline. *American Journal of Community Psychology* **21**(3):333–59.

Weitz, R (1989). Uncertainty and the lives of persons with AIDS. *Journal of Health and Social Behavior* **30**:270–81.

Williams, C (1994). Sex education and the AIDS epidemic in the former Soviet Union. *Sociology of Health and Illness* **16**(1):81.

Williams, F (1992). *Structural Inequalities and the Management of Personal Welfare: a Selective Literature Review and Assessment*. ESRC 'Management of Personal Welfare' Inequalities Theme. ESRC report.

Williams, G, Popay, J and Bissell, P (1995). Public health risks in the material world: barriers to social movements in health. In Gabe, J (ed.) *Medicine, Health and Risks*. Blackwell.

Williams, G H and Wood, P H N (1986). Patients and their illnesses: common-sense beliefs about illnesses: a mediating role for the doctor. *Lancet* December 20/27, p. 1435.

Wright, A L and Morgan, W J (1990). On the creation of 'problem' patients. *Social Science and Medicine* **30**(9):951–9.

Young, H and Jaspars, S (1995). Nutritional assessments, food security and famine. *Disasters* **19**(1):26–36.

Young, J C (1981). Non-use of physicians: methodological approaches, policy implications, and the utility of decision models. *Social Science and Medicine* **15B**:499–507.

Zola, I K (1966). Culture and symptoms – an analysis of patients' presenting complaints. *American Sociological Review* **31**:615–30.